CLIMB INJU

A Proven Injury Prevention and Rehabilitation System

DR. JARED VAGY DPT

Doctor of Physical Therapy
Board Certified Clinical Specialist

info@theclimbingdoctor.com
www.theclimbingdoctor.com

Content Photography: Stephen Gross, Matthew Johnson and Ari Kirsch
Graphic Design and Cover: Rachelle Vagy
Climbers: Sasha Digiulian, Josh Levin, Sean McColl and Jonathan Siegrist
Editors: Alex Gullen, Dominik Sklarzyk and Hayden Carpenter

Dedication
Rick Vagy, Sharyl Vagy, Rachelle Vagy, Grandma Claire, Grandpa Sid, Grandma Sylvia and Shawn Goodman.

Acknowledgments
To those who have helped or inspired me along the long journey of life, climbing and making this book a reality: Adidas, Mike Andersen, Mike Anderson, Arc'teryx, The Banff Center, Steve Bechtel, Justin Bieber, Joven Borro, Phil Bridgers, Climb Magazine, Climbing Magazine, Christian Core, Steph Davis, Sander DiAngelis, Sasha DiGiulian, Julie Ellison, Jeremy Eng, Kat Eng, EpicTV, Clare Frank, George Goodman, Jim Gordon, Jacob Haas, Erik Hörst, Hazel Findlay, Hans Florine, Miguel Forjan, Nick Gerrard, Joe Godges, Planet Granite, Neil Gresham, Steve Grosserode, Lynn Hill, Cliffs of Id, Chris Kalous, Dan Kirages, Jason Kutch, Rob Landel, Lea Leopoldo, Josh Levin, John Long, Eva Lopez, Tanya Mackenzie, Dana Mackison, Sean McColl, Dan Mirsky, Tara Misiewicz, Norman Montes, Chris Neve, Adam Ondra, Petzl, David Pickford, Ethan Pringle, Neely Quinn, Rick Rafael, Steve Reischl, Paul Robinson, Rock and Ice Magazine, Rockreation, Ben Rueck, Matt Samet, Volker Schöffl, Matt Segal, Linda Shigetomi, Jonathan Siegrist, Mayan Smith-Gobat, Matt Stark, Touchstone Climbing, Theraband, Earth Treks, Sonnie Trotter, Vasya Vorotnikov, Mike Williams, Ken Yager, Bill Zimmermann and the many others I have forgotten to mention.

CHAPTER 1: THE APPROACH

CHAPTER 2: PREVENT INJURY

CHAPTER 3: THE ROCK REHAB PYRAMID

CHAPTER 4: NECK AND SHOULDER REHABILITATION

CHAPTER 5: ELBOW REHABILITATION

CHAPTER 6: WRIST AND FINGERS REHABILITATION

CHAPTER 7: NERVE MOBILITY

CHAPTER 8: THE DESCENT

SASHA DIGIULIAN

First North American Woman to Climb 5.14D, Indoor Climbing Overall World Champion

When I first started rock climbing at age 6, 16 years ago, I only climbed. I didn't train specifically for performance or injury prevention. I would just climb five days a week. Then I suffered through a series of injuries that set back my progress as a climber. I fell and cracked my L4 vertebrae, tore three ligaments in my ankle and ruptured the A2 pulley in my left ring finger. Only then did I realize I needed to be cognizant of how I was taking care of my body, and what I was doing to prevent and recover from injuries.

As I grew older, my body began to change as well. I overdeveloped the muscles used specifically for climbing—such as my biceps, deltoids (shoulders) and lats (back)—and left lagging far behind my non-climbing-specific muscles. This created an imbalance.

Over time I learned that strengthening my oppositional muscles, while it would help, wouldn't alone prevent injury. I also needed to be more aware of my movement patterns on the wall and understand the relationship of how repeated movements can stress or injure different areas of the body.

The science of training was completely new to me, but having started recently along this path, I have already seen progressive gains in not only my health, but also my climbing. In the past year before I started sport-specific training, I was stuck at a plateau. I wasn't seeing any meaningful gains and I would always finish a day with aches and pains. Once I started to incorporate dynamic warm-ups, oppositional-muscle strengthening and climbing-specific exercises, I finally broke through this plateau. More importantly, I am far less prone to climbing injuries.

This book, based on the latest research, will give you the tools you need to take your climbing to the next level without getting hurt.

Sasha Digiulian on Dures Limites 5.14b (8c). Ceuse, France. Photo Credit: Jensen Walker

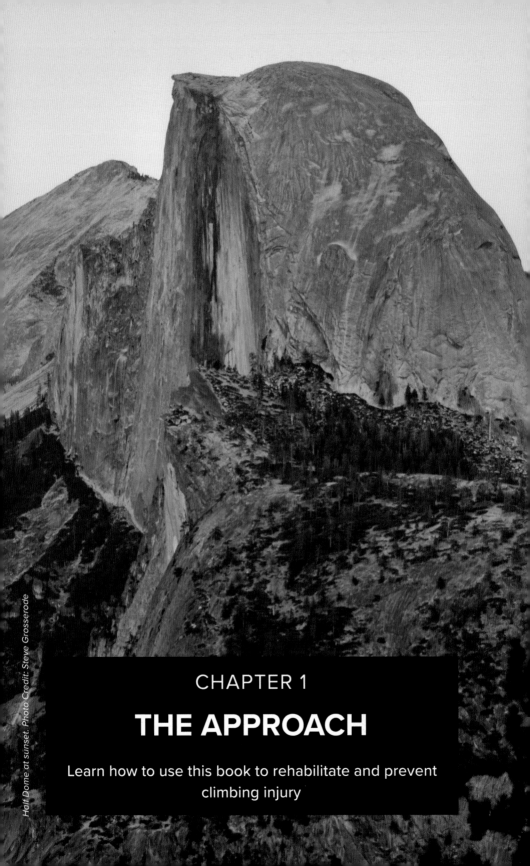

CHAPTER 1

THE APPROACH

Learn how to use this book to rehabilitate and prevent climbing injury

THE CLIMBING DOCTOR STORY

I was hooked on climbing the second I touched a rock wall. I would spend long days climbing and training as much as possible. I was climbing hard but I wasn't listening to my body. Because of overtraining, I tore a pulley ligament in my finger and injured the rotator cuff muscles in my shoulder, sidelining me from climbing for many months.

During this time, I was completing my Doctorate Degree in Physical Therapy. Through my studies I recognized several problems with my training and learned the science behind my injuries. I developed new techniques supported by the latest research and created specific exercises to mirror the movements that climbers perform. I took this knowledge, first for myself, and then began treating other injured climbers.

I wanted everyone to have this knowledge, so I created The Rock Rehab Pyramid. A science-based system that all climbers could learn, understand, and use on their own to prevent injuries and rehabilitate.

Summit of La Esfinge in Peru: 5.10d R at 17,470 feet

HOW TO USE THE BOOK

This book is for climbers of all ability levels and will teach you how to climb injury-free. You will learn through a series of chapters how to prevent injuries from occurring and how to rehabilitate the 10 most common climbing injuries. Step-by-step instructions will take you through the process. The material in this book was developed from the combination of thousands of hours of clinical expertise treating climbing injuries and over 14 years of climbing experience as a rock climber of all disciplines (trad, sport, boulder, aid and big wall). It utilizes the latest research developments in rehabilitation and movement science. The book is divided into 7 chapters.

Chapter 1: The Approach
Provides you with the framework necessary to implement the prevention and rehabilitation exercises in the book.

Chapter 2: Prevent Injury
Teaches you the fundamentals to ensure you continue to climb without injury. Six guidelines are introduced to give a greater perspective on how to prevent injury. Injury-prevention warm-ups are thoroughly explained with concepts of dynamic stretching and muscle activation. A daily prevention program is introduced that targets both flexibility and antagonist strengthening to give you a foundation for climbing injury-free. Functional exercises that look and feel like climbing are introduced. Movement education is described to ensure proper climbing technique. Lastly, mind and body discussions are introduced to increase the awareness of diet, sleep and training capacity.

Chapter 3: The Rock Rehab Pyramid
Introduces a framework to self-manage climbing injuries. The pyramid is described and then applied to the 10 most common climbing injuries. Concepts of tissue unloading, mobility, strength and movement re-education are all discussed in detail, teaching you how to rehabilitate your own injuries.

Chapter 4: Neck and Shoulder Rehabilitation
Outlines in detail the most effective way to rehabilitate neck strain, rotator cuff strain and shoulder impingement.

Chapter 5: Elbow Rehabilitation
Outlines in detail the most effective way to rehabilitate biceps tendinopathy, triceps tendinopathy, lateral epicondylosis and medial epicondylosis.

Chapter 6: Wrist and Finger Rehabilitation

Outlines in detail the most effective way to rehabilitate carpal tunnel syndrome, finger pulley sprain and finger collateral ligament sprain.

Chapter 7: Nerve Mobility

Outlines the concept of neurodynamics and how to use mobilization exercises to treat nerve pain.

Chapter 8: The Descent

Provides an appendix of rehabilitation pyramids, references, climber biographies and author biographies.

Beyond the Scope of the Book

Always consult your physician or physical therapist before beginning any exercise program. That said, it is equally important to seek medical advice from a person who is both a medical professional and a climber. A medical professional who is a climber will understand climbing movement, the unique physical demands and injuries of the sport, and your eagerness to get back on the rock.

What type of medical professional should you choose? Injury diagnosis and rehabilitation is a multidisciplinary approach that may include a physician, surgeon, physical therapist, athletic trainer, chiropractor, acupuncturist, mental health professional, dietitian or any other wellness/medical professional. From whom you seek advice depends on your injury.

For example, if you have a severe pulley tear and the tendon is bowstringing away from your bone, you should see an orthopedic hand surgeon. If you have a movement dysfunction, you should see a doctor of physical therapy.

Doctors of physical therapy are the medical professionals who have the greatest background in movement science. The educational process consists of seven years of university-level academics. Some advance their degrees (like myself) with an additional two years of residency and fellowship training to further specialize their skills. Whichever medical professional you choose to see, it may be helpful to bring with you a copy of this book as a starting point to discuss your injury.

REHABILITATE CLIMBING INJURIES

This book will walk you through rehabilitation for the 10 most common climbing injuries, including: belayer's neck, rotator cuff strain, shoulder impingement, biceps tendinopathy, triceps tendinopathy, lateral epicondylosis, medial epicondylosis, carpal tunnel syndrome, pulley sprain and collateral ligament sprain.

Each chapter first introduces the description, signs and symptoms, and cause of an injury, followed by a color-coded progression through the rehabilitation pyramid.

Techniques described in red are for UNLOADING

Techniques described in purple are for MOBILITY

Techniques described in blue are for STRENGTH

Techniques described in green are for MOVEMENT

Each technique is thoroughly described with instructions of what the exercise does and the frequency at which to perform it.

Individualized treatment plans are outside the scope of this book because of the high variability of personal injury. However, general guidelines are given that are based on tissue adaptation stages and principals.

You can perform tissue unloading for as long as it takes for your pain at rest to subside; mobility exercises up to three times per day; and strength exercises daily. Movement advice should be used every time you climb.

Pro Advice

This book contains not only my opinions on rehabilitation, but also the consensus of the climbing community. With this in mind, I thought it was important to include the viewpoints of climbers who are performing at the highest level. I interviewed several of the top climbers in the world, many of whom are my clients, to explore their thoughts and opinions on how to rehabilitate injuries. Interspersed throughout this book are over 30 full-page photo spreads that include the thoughts and experiences of these pros on preventing injuries and rehabilitation.

EQUIPMENT RECOMMENDATIONS AND DIRTBAG TIPS

Equipment Recommendations

There are several rehabilitation tools that are utilized in this book to perform targeted exercises. Having the proper tool can make a big difference in your rehabilitation results. Much like having the correct piece of gear to put in a crack when you are 30 feet run-out from your last piece.

Of all the tools listed, a lacrosse ball and a set of resistance bands would be the highest on the recommendation list to purchase. They are cheap, versatile and portable.

Dirtbag Tips

> **DIRTBAG TIPS**
> Look out for "Dirtbag Tips" that are scattered throughout the book. These blue boxes will give you cheap and easy ways to convert your climbing gear or household items into rehab tools without the need for any specialized equipment.

If you can't afford rehabilitation tools, you are in luck. I understand the financial plight of a dirtbag climber. A few years after I began practicing as a doctor of physical therapy, I quit my job to pursue climbing full time.

My dirtbag dreams, however, came to an end six months later. My professional path led me astray from the rootless lifestyle and into higher-level education. The fondness I retain for those months spent pursuing nothing other than climbing remains undiminished.

As such, I created this book with regard for the dirtbag. Almost all rehabilitation tools described in this book can be substituted with household items or retired climbing gear. Below is an example of a "Dirtbag Tip."

> **DIRTBAG TIPS EXAMPLE**
> Instead of using a foam roll, you can use a coiled climbing rope or two large bath towels rolled up and placed at the center of your spine.

See pages 16 and 17 for additional suggestions of rehab tool substitutions that are used throughout the book.

REHAB TOOL	DIRTBAG SUBSTITUTION
TheraBand	Climbing Webbing
FlexBar	Rolled Towel
Foam Roll	Rope or Rolled Bath Towel
Baoding Balls	Two Rocks

REHAB TOOL	DIRTBAG SUBSTITUTION
Arm Aid	Lacrosse Ball or Smooth Rock
Big Wall Hammer	Wine Bottle or Frying Pan
Slider	Paper Plate or Sock
Hand Xtrainer	Rubber-Band

DIAGNOSE YOUR INJURY

Use the diagrams below to identify the region and associated medical terminology of your injury.

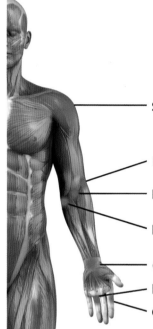

Shoulder Impingement: Pages 100-118

Lateral Epicondylosis: Pages 141-156

Biceps Tendinopathy: Pages 120-129

Medial Epicondylosis: Pages 157-166

Carpal Tunnel Syndrome: Pages 168-182

Pulley Sprain: Pages 184-203

Collateral Ligament Sprain: Pages 204-214

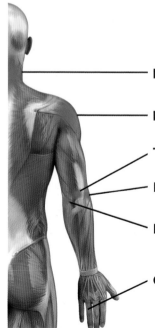

Neck Strain: Pages 70-84

Rotator Cuff Strain: Pages 86-99

Triceps Tendinopathy: Pages 130-140

Lateral Epicondylosis: Pages 141-156

Medial Epicondylosis: Pages 157-166

Collateral Ligament Sprain: Pages 204-214

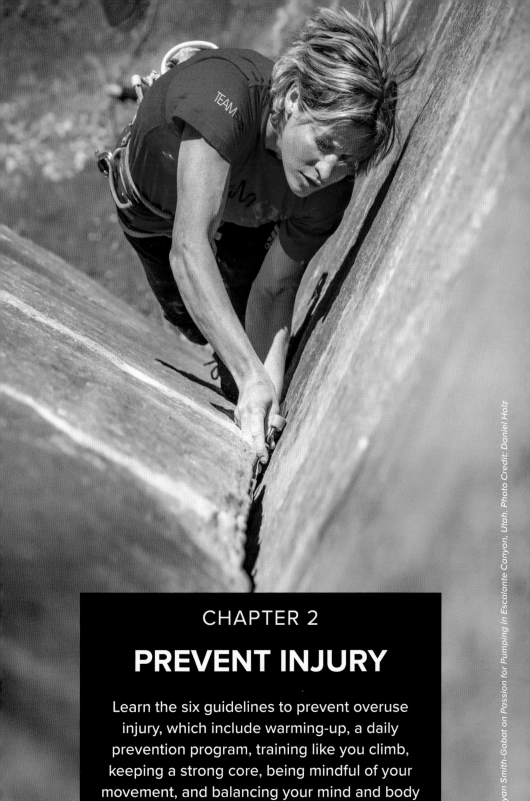

Mayan Smith-Gobat on Passion for Pumping in Escalante Canyon, Utah. Photo Credit: Daniel Holz

CHAPTER 2

PREVENT INJURY

Learn the six guidelines to prevent overuse injury, which include warming-up, a daily prevention program, training like you climb, keeping a strong core, being mindful of your movement, and balancing your mind and body

6 GUIDELINES TO PREVENT OVERUSE INJURY

Analysis Paralysis
Learning about how to prevent injuries can be intimidating and confusing if you don't have a set of guidelines to direct you. Where do you start? How do you know which exercises to choose? Whose advice is best to follow?

Enter "rock climbing injury prevention" into an Internet search query and you will find hundreds of articles (many of them my own) on how to prevent climbing injuries. Figuring out how best to start the process and progress thereafter can be an overwhelming and difficult task.

Targeted Prevention
To reduce such complexity I have developed six guidelines that will help guide you through the injury-prevention process. Each of these guidelines might seem obvious, but if you apply them consistently within a comprehensive program, you will decrease your injury risk and climb more efficiently.

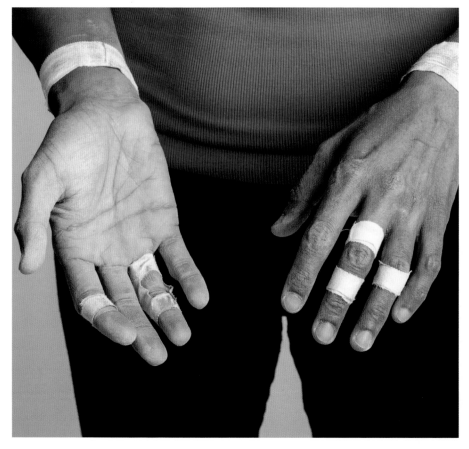

1. Warm-up Properly

Dynamic Warm-up
Statically stretching before climbing is dangerous. It can lead to decreased muscle strength and even injury. It is important to perform dynamic stretching instead, 10 minutes prior to commencement of climbing. Dynamic stretching increases the blood-flow to your muscles, tendons and joints and can help prevent injury.

Muscle Activation
Muscle-activation exercises are used to turn on your oppositional muscles, which are essential for injury prevention. By using low resistance and sustained holds, you can "wake-up" these muscles prior to climbing.

2. Perform a Daily Prevention Program

Stretching
Your muscles tend to overwork from the repetitive nature of climbing and will become even stiffer through poor posture. Tight muscles can pull on and strain the tendons where they attach to the bone. They can also create increased resistance to movement. By performing regular stretching you will increase your flexibility and thus decrease the tension in your muscles. Stretching before climbing should always be dynamic. However, stretching any other time can be a combination of both static and dynamic

Antagonistic Exercises
Antagonist muscles naturally oppose the muscles that we primarily use to climb. They affect movement in the opposite direction. Weak antagonist muscles leave you highly susceptible to overuse injury. By strengthening these muscles, you will balance your body and decrease the likelihood of getting hurt while climbing.

3. Train Like You Climb

Mirroring Movement
Many training exercises don't reflect your body's position or the demand on your body while climbing and therefore don't translate into meaningful climbing improvements. In order for an exercise to properly transpose into your climbing, the body position in the exercise must be similar to the body position when you climb. You will have more meaningful results from exercises and a greater "carryover" if the movements resemble climbing.

4. Keep a Strong Core

The 4 Core Categories

It is important to realize that the climbing core is not just the abdominal muscles in the front of your body. The climber's core involves the midsection, the shoulder blades and the hips. When training the core, you need to forget about "old-school" exercises such as crunches and begin to perform exercises that incorporate the entire "climber's core."

5. Be Mindful of Your Movement

Correct Climbing Technique

You can perform every rehabilitation exercise in this book and still have pain if you don't identify the cause of your pain in the first place. When you are mindful of your movement, you can identify dangerous movements that you are performing while climbing and correct them to take stress off your body. There are five key concepts to keep in mind when climbing. Make sure to keep good posture, bring your hips into the wall, straighten your arms, push with your feet and climb like you crawl.

6. Balance Your Mind and Body

The Teeter-Totter Theory

There is a fine balance between having a healthy mind and body when it comes to climbing. The mental and physical aspects of climbing must complement each other in order to climb injury-free at a high level.

It is easy to become too cerebral and fill the mind with fear and self-doubt. This naturally imposes a high level of caution with respect to decision making and can lead to a climber never fulfilling their true potential. In contrast, if a climber trains too much and focuses all of their energy on improving the physical but doesn't address their mental game, they can over train, burnout and get hurt.

To climb at a high level without injury you need to have balance. When the mind and body connect, you begin to listen more carefully to the signals that your body sends.

1. WARM-UP PROPERLY

Most climbers understand the importance of warming-up before climbing, but not all climbers understand what type of warm-up is the best. Before learning how to warm-up properly, it is important to understand the different ways that you can warm-up and prepare your body for climbing.

What is static, ballistic and dynamic stretching?

Static stretching is when you hold a single position to achieve a stretch. Common hold times are around 30 seconds. An example is bending down to touch your toes and holding.

Ballistic stretching is when you bounce in and out of a position to achieve a stretch. Common hold times are less than a second. An example is bending down to touch your toes and bouncing quickly several times at the bottom of the stretch.

Dynamic stretching is when you smoothly move through a full range of motion spending equal time in each phase of the stretch. An example is bending down to touch your toes while counting to three and coming back up to standing while counting to three.

How to stretch before climbing?

Static stretching is a poor choice: A static stretch of a muscle before activity can impair muscle strength and leads to decreased performance. This can actually increase injury rate.

Ballistic stretching is a poor choice: A ballistic stretch can be hazardous when used as a warm-up. The rapid nature of the movement activates a reflex in the muscle causing it to contract to protect itself from harm. This can cause micro-tearing of the muscle.

Dynamic stretching is the best choice: A dynamic warm-up is the best way to increase blood flow to the muscles and tendons in the body. This method prepares the body for a specific activity and can help reduce injury rates.

The Dynamic Warm-up and Slider Series

The Dynamic Climbing Warm-up

The climbing-specific dynamic warm-up is broken down into four stages. The goal is to increase blood flow and warmth to your body while mirroring climbing-specific positions.

Stage 1: On the Wall

The entire body mirrors those positions that are used while climbing.

Stage 2: Rotation

Rotational movements to warm-up the joints.

Stage 3: Upper Body

Dynamic stretching to warm a primary muscle and its opposing muscle.

Stage 4: Wrist and Fingers

Targets the smallest muscle groups with tendon glides.

After this warm-up, climb two to four easy routes in a range two number grades below your consistent climbing grade. For example, if you climb 5.10, warm-up on two routes of 5.8.

The Slider Series

The climbing-specific slider series was developed to provide a transition from standing exercises to ones that involve weight bearing on all four limbs. By using sliders in climbing-specific positions on the ground, you are forced to recruit your muscles in a similar manner to how you use them when climbing.

The key exercises used in this sequence are body opener, frogger, flag, reverse outside flag and high step. You can get creative and start to mirror even more positions with the sliders. You can even map out certain moves and sequences that you would encounter on the route that you are climbing or projecting.

The slider series is used mostly to warm-up, but as you become comfortable with performing exercises on your hands and knees, you will begin to realize the possibilities of using the on-ground positions for performance training.

DAN MIRSKY
5.14c Sport Climb First Ascensionist

A proper warm-up is perhaps the most important thing I do to keep climbing injury-free. I warm-up for 30 minutes every day before I climb. Dynamic stretching always feels like a great way to awaken my body. My fingers are always a critical part of my pre-climbing warm-up. I do a number of different range of motion exercises to begin to activate my fingers. The best are the "tendon glides" I learned from the Climbing Doctor. When I am ready to ramp it up a bit, I move into something more climbing specific. My go-to tools are a rice bucket, a set of TheraBands and a Flexbar. Although it seems like a lot, an extra 30 minutes is a small amount of time when compared to the months of no climbing that can result from some injuries. I have found that if I warm-up well, I can definitely see the benefit in my performance. I can climb harder and longer before I start to feel fatigue. After the climbing is done and I am relaxing with a cold beer, feeling tired and happy, I try to remind myself, regardless of what did happen climbing, the most important thing I got from my warm-up that day is what didn't happen; an injury.

Dan Mirsky on the first ascent of Solid Gold, 5.14c. Welcome Springs, Utah. Photo Credit: Luke Olson

The Dynamic Climbing Warm-up

Below is an example of a dynamic climbing warm-up. The aim is to move between the various warm-up postures illustrated in a rhythmical, slow and controlled motion repeating each posture 5 times per side. The detailed video-based warm-up can be viewed at: **theclimbingdoctor.com/warm-up**

The Slider Series

This program can be used to supplement your dynamic warm-up by mirroring movements on the ground that you would perform whilst climbing.

> **DIRTBAG TIPS**
> Instead of purchasing furniture sliders, you can use common household items instead. When performing on hardwood floors you can wear thick cotton sweatpants and use socks or gloves on your hands. When performing on carpet you can use paper plates underneath both your hands and knees.

Body Opener
A Begin on hands and knees.
B Sit your bottom back and reach both arms together fully overhead while bending your torso to the side. Use your abdominal muscles to sweep your arms and torso to the other side. You should feel a stretch through the side of the arms and torso.

Frogger
A Begin on hands and knees.
B Bring your knees out to the side as your arms reach to the side and overhead. You should feel a stretch in the groin. Contract the abdominal muscles and inner thigh muscles to return to your starting position.

Flag and Reverse Outside Flag

A Place one slider under your left knee and the others under your right foot and both hands. Reach your right arm overhead and to the right as your right foot sweeps to the left to mirror a reverse outside flag.

B Reach your left arm overhead and to the left and you reach your right foot over to the right to mirror a standard flag. Perform on both sides.

High Step

A Place one slider under your left knee and the others under your right foot and both hands.

B Reach both arms overhead as you drive your right knee towards your chest and your left knee backwards.

C Reverse the motion and press your right leg back as your left knee drives towards your chest. Perform on both sides.

Muscle Activation

Climbing is a sport that develops many of the muscles that hunch your body forward into a poor posture. This is why climbers begin to develop curved spines and arms that rotate in. This hunched position can lead to weakness of the postural muscles that oppose typical climbing movement. These oppositional muscles are known as antagonist muscles. The development of antagonist muscles is necessary to protect your body from injury while climbing and belaying.

The key is to activate antagonist muscles prior to climbing. You can do so by maintaining sustained pressure against a light resistance band for up to one minute. This increased duration of time allows you to develop a brain-body connection and will "wake up" the muscles. A British study in 2000 by Doran et al. identified that over 40% of climbing injuries occur in the hand. Many of these hand injuries are caused by improper movements in the lower body. Therefore, it is essential that the lower body kinetic chain muscles are also incorporated into the position. The next page shows you how to wrap a TheraBand across the body to activate the antagonist muscles in the hip, shoulders, elbows and wrists.

The Activation Position

Instructions
A Stand on a TheraBand and loop it in front of the lower legs making a cross.
B Behind the thighs making another cross.
C In front of the thighs making a final cross.
D Rotate your palms inward facing your body.
E Wrap your fingers down and around the band.
F Hold the position with your shoulders rotated out and fingers extended.

What It Does
This exercise is best done after your dynamic warm-up and prior to climbing to "activate" the antagonist muscles that protect your body when you climb.

Frequency
30 second hold prior to climbing. Repeat for 3-5 sets.

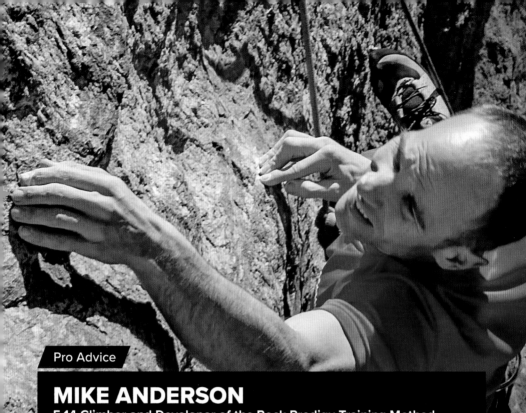

MIKE ANDERSON
5.14 Climber and Developer of the Rock Prodigy Training Method

Muscle Activation is an excellent warm-up activity that can also be applied to hangboard training. When I attended Dr. Vagy's seminar and learned about the value of muscle activation, I immediately thought about adapting it to hangboard training. For years now, I've struggled with training my one finger, or "mono pocket" grip because it is very tweaky and susceptible to injury. I was always flirting with injuries and would often get tweaks that would set back my training and erode my confidence, preventing me from pushing myself in that grip.

I tried muscle activation by performing one 10-second hang then one 30-second hang on the mono grip at a low intensity (about 70% of my training intensity). I would perform this during every workout, minutes before my mono training sets.

The results were great! This warm-up drastically reduced the tweaks I would encounter in my higher-intensity training sets, allowing me to push much harder. Also, the activation, and recruiting of the muscle fibers, made me better-prepared for the training so I could generate more force. I've done this through two training seasons now, and I've made personal bests on that grip as a result. I can now hang more weight from my monos than I ever could before. I now do this preparation for multiple grips, and I highly recommend it. I use it to warm-up for bouldering and routes, as well any time I expect tweaky holds.

Mike on Mission Impossible, 5.14c. Clear Creek Canyon, Colorado. Photo Credit: Chris Alstrin

2. PERFORM A DAILY PREVENTION PROGRAM

The Importance of Daily Prevention

You may feel that injuries aren't going to happen to you. But once they occur, prevention effort is too little too late. It is much smarter to prevent injuries than deal with the consequences. Preventing climbing injuries is not hard to do. It just takes an awareness of your movements and less than 20 minutes a day of supplemental exercises.

Injury-prevention exercises should develop into a habit just like brushing your teeth. Imagine how your breath would smell and how rotten your teeth would be if you only ate food but never brushed your teeth. The same goes for corrective exercises. If you only climb and don't perform corrective exercises to balance your body, you will start to breakdown and can get injured. A daily prevention program goes a long way and can keep you out of serious trouble.

Exercise Selection

The stretching exercises target the pectoralis and latissimus dorsi muscles. These are muscles that, when stiff, can lead to a hunched climber body. The antagonist-muscle exercises focus on the shoulder blade retractors (middle trapezius and rhomboids), external rotator cuff (infraspinatus and teres minor), wrist and finger extensors. These are the muscles that can prevent overuse climbing injuries.

Progression and Sequence

The daily prevention program can be performed in less than 20 minutes. Each of the five stretches and antagonist exercises are performed for 1 minute each for two sets. Stretching exercises are performed first to increase your range of motion. Muscle-activation exercises are then performed to strengthen your antagonist muscles to balance the body.

Piggy-Back on a Habit

Incorporating a daily prevention program into your busy life is a challenge. Old habits are hard to break and new habits are difficult to keep. One tip that can help you integrate a new habit into your daily life is to perform it directly after a habit that already exists. Linking prevention exercises to a deeply embedded daily task such as brushing your teeth, getting dressed in the morning or even during a regularly scheduled lunch break can help ingrain them further.

Stretching

It is important to stretch the stiff muscles in your body to increase flexibility and prevent injury. Stretching before climbing should always be dynamic. However, stretching any other time can be a combination of both static and dynamic. The stretching program below can be performed up to three times each day. It is recommended to use a six-inch diameter foam roll, however there are several other alternatives that you can use.

DIRTBAG TIPS
Instead of using a foam roll, you can use a coiled climbing rope or two large bath towels rolled up and placed at the center of your spine.

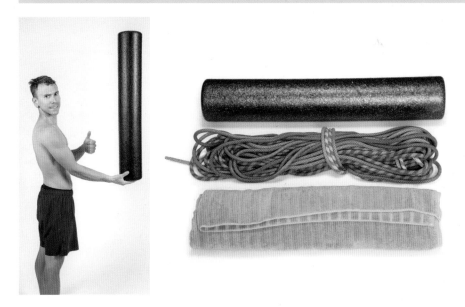

Many climbers perform the following stretches incorrectly by flaring out their rib cage and arching their low back. Make sure to keep your ribcage down and back flat as shown in the photos. This can be accomplished by activating your abdominal muscles during the stretches. If it is a challenge to keep your abdominals engaged while stretching, exhale each time you lift your arms overhead. This will naturally bring your ribs downwards and improve the form of the stretch.

Stretch before performing your antagonist-muscle exercises. This will increase your available range of motion so that you can take advantage of your improved flexibility when performing the antagonist exercises.

JOSH LEVIN
19-Time Youth National Champion

I was fortunate to find my passion for climbing at a very early age. With the support from my parents, I began climbing outdoors at age 6 and started competing on the national and international level by the time I was 8. For most of my career up until recently, I've been able to avoid many common injuries by performing a proper and thorough warm-up. Every single time I get on the wall, I always try and think how to properly warm-up for the specific climbing situation I am in. My routine has been one of the biggest reasons I've been able to stay injury-free up until this point.

The first component to warming-up is to increase blood flow to muscles, tendons and joints. Utilizing full-body aerobic activities such as jogging or performing jumping jacks really helps get the heart pumping and the blood flowing. After your heart rate is up, it is then important to perform dynamic stretches. You should follow dynamic stretching with some type of muscle-activation training. Push your arms isometrically against the wall or use resistance bands to activate the muscle prior to climbing. After completing the aerobic, dynamic stretching and muscle-activation components of the warm-up, climb an easy lap around the wall. Make sure your shoes are working correctly, check your chalk amount and dial in your breathing rhythm. One trick that I learned from Dr. Vagy is to pause for two minutes during my traverse on an overhanging jug and to engage my postural muscles by squeezing my shoulder blades together. This activates the muscles, reinforces proper body position and helps break the bad habit of climbing with a slumped posture.

Although my general approach to warming-up for each discipline of climbing is similar, the details are different. For example, I warm-up for a speed climbing competition very differently than I do for a bouldering or sport climbing competition. For speed climbing it is important to focus heavily on the aerobic warm-up as well as increasing the tempo of the dynamic stretches to activate the fast-twitch muscle fibers. For sport climbing competitions put extra effort into stretching the legs because of the importance of achieving unique resting positions on the wall. For bouldering an even more rigorous warm-up is recommended because of the powerful nature of many of the moves. It is key to perform a lot of extra finger exercises such as finger flicks up and tendon glides.

If you don't do one of those components correctly it could lead to not getting enough blood flow, not stretching the right body component or not activating the right muscles before you get on the wall. Not performing a thorough warm-up actually led to one of my injuries, so now I am highly diligent about taking the necessary steps to warm-up properly so I can climb injury-free.

Josh Levin winning the Dominion Riverrock Speed Bouldering Competition. Photo Credit: Jesse Peters

Overhead Arms - *Dynamic stretch: Keep the stomach engaged and back flat*
Alternate raising each arm above your head as your opposite arm reaches
down by your side. Engage your core and exhale while reaching. Make sure
your thumb is directed towards the floor when reaching overhead.

Lizards - *Dynamic stretch: Keep the stomach engaged and back flat*
Begin with both elbows bent to 90 degrees and at shoulder height. Alternate
moving each arm overhead towards your ear as the other arm moves towards
your torso. Maintain your elbow bend at 90 degrees throughout the exercise.

Touchdowns - *Dynamic stretch: Keep the stomach engaged and back flat*
Begin with both elbows bent to 90 degrees and at shoulder height. Move both
arms overhead while straightening your elbows.

T Stretch - *Static stretch: Keep the stomach engaged and back flat*
Relax both arms perpendicular to your body to form the letter T.

Y Stretch - *Static stretch: Keep the stomach engaged and back flat*
Relax both arms above your head to form the letter Y.

Antagonist Exercises

**Band Reaches:
Page 94**

**Letter T:
Page 110**

**Wall Angel:
Page 107-108**

Weighted Dowel: Page 151

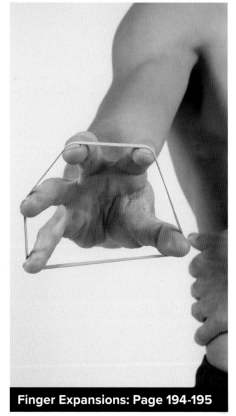

Finger Expansions: Page 194-195

Stretching Quick Reference

Overhead Arms

Lizards

Touchdowns

T Stretch

Y Stretch

Antagonist Exercises Quick Reference

Wall Angel

Band Reaches

Letter T

Weighted Dowel

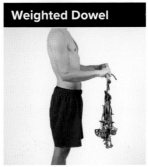

Finger Expansions

ADAM ONDRA
5.15c Climber and First Ascents, 3-Time World Champion In Lead, Boulder and Overall

I started climbing at a very young age and my progress has been steady, but relatively slow. My steady progression over time has allowed my body to perfectly adapt to the demands of climbing.

I have been climbing for over 16 years now and I have never had any major injuries. Is it luck? Is it genetics? Or is it because I take the necessary steps daily to prevent injury? It is hard to tell, but I suspect the latter.

When preventing injuries there are several important things to consider. One of the most crucial skills to have is to know when you need to stop. Most injuries can be avoided if you take two days of rest once you start feeling the pain. How do you know whether you're just tired and sore or you are injured? It is often hard to discern between whether you are feeling a healthy fatigue or a dangerous pain. Only with time, careful consideration and by listening to your body can you begin to distinguish the two. Using pain killers to block the pain and continuing to climb will get you in trouble. It is important to know that pain is a warning signal from the brain. We need to listen to it and not ignore it.

Stretching and performing antagonist-muscle exercises are also very important when training to prevent climbing injuries. I have been to physios quite a few times and have learned various stretches and antagonist-muscle exercises. The exercises worked very well.

Another option is to train using a TRX suspension trainer. It is essentially two hanging strands of webbing anchored at a fixed point. You can use it for antagonist muscle exercises as seen on pages 114 and 115. Although some climbers are lazy to perform antagonist-muscle exercises, most of the climbers are not that lazy to train hard. So this is a good alternative and can make you climb harder too.

Most of the things that will help you avoid injuries will also help you climb harder. No matter how hard you train, you won't be able to climb anything if you are hurt. Healthy is strong, which is a good mantra to remember when performing injury-prevention exercises. When your body is in sync and feeling strong you will climb your hardest.

Adam Ondra on Vicious Circle, 5.15a/b (9a+/b). Tadej's cave, Slovenia. Photo Credit: Javipec

3. TRAIN LIKE YOU CLIMB

Climbing-Specific Exercise Examples

Make sure that you supplement your training program with climbing-specific exercises. Climbing-specific exercises simulate the movements and physical demands of climbing.

The exercises below are a few examples of how you can develop exercises on the ground to mirror climbing-specific movements.

Drop Knee: Climbing

Drop Knee: Band Press

Drop Knee: Triceps Extension

Reverse Outside Flag: Climbing

Reverse Outside Flag: Band Press

Reverse Outside Flag: Stick Press

Mirroring Movement

Train More Effectively with Climbing-Specific Exercises
In order for an exercise to carry over to climbing, the body position in the exercise must be similar to the body position when you climb. By paying careful attention to the position of your body from toes to fingertips, you can make dramatic changes in the effectiveness of your training exercises.

6 Exercise Rules to Mirror Climbing Movement
I've developed six rules that can be applied to any typical exercise to make it more climbing specific. The rules will help you adapt exercises to support you climbing even harder without getting hurt. Each of these rules should seem intuitive. However, if you analyze your own training exercises, you will likely find that very few of your exercises satisfy all of these rules. The more an exercise resembles your movement in a given sport, the more the exercise positively affects your performance in that sport. Simply put, make your exercises mirror climbing.

1. Put Weight into Your Toes
When climbing, you rarely transfer full weight into the heels unless you are using a heel hook, backstepping, standing on a huge ledge or are in a chimney. With stemming, corners, face climbing, steep roofs, or even crack climbing, your toes do most of the work to power your legs and balance on holds. So when training for climbing, it is important to shift the weight into your toes. You can balance with one or both legs on a step or a small platform. Too easy? Close your eyes while performing a flag maneuver. If a step is not available, you can always repeatedly stand up and down on your toes to build endurance in your calf muscles.

2. Bend Your Knees
On the rock wall, you must bend your knees in order to transfer weight into your strong legs and out of your arms. Your body's most powerful muscles are in the legs. They are designed to support and transfer your weight. Your arms are not designed to do that. In order to replicate climbing movement, do exercises that train your knees to bend while your arms reach or pull. Try to perform your arm exercises while in a squat position, rather than standing upright. This will train your leg muscles to engage during arm movement.

3. Engage Your Abdominals

Maintaining core tension while climbing allows for an effective transfer of forces from the feet to the hands. The more stable your midsection the more you are able to utilize small holds and pull harder moves. The improved transfer of force allows you to climb more efficiently. The core muscles are rarely used to initiate movement, so stay away from exercises such as crunches that don't resemble climbing. Focus more on exercises that keep a stable midsection while performing arm or leg movements. For example, lie on your back, keep a neutral spine and circle your arms and legs in the air, mimicking the way your body moves when you climb.

4. Stabilize Your Shoulder Blades

The shoulder blade muscles provide the foundation for moving your arms. When the muscles engage, they take the stress off of the arms. To demonstrate this, raise a weight to shoulder height with your shoulder blades slumped forward and then lift the same weight with your shoulder blades engaged. Which one is easier? You will notice the weight feels lighter to lift with the shoulder blades stabilized. This is because when you engage your large shoulder blade muscles, you add additional support to your arm. Keep your shoulder blades engaged when you are training and climbing. Even better, remember to keep good posture the 22 hours that you are not climbing. Try sleeping on your back, instead of your side. This promotes an open chest and allows gravity to retract your shoulder blades while you sleep.

5. Keep Your Hands Above Your Shoulders

The majority of climbing involves hands positioned above shoulder height. There are few instances when you climb, such as on mantles and low underclings, when the hands work below shoulder height. Exercises with hands below the shoulders translate poorly to climbing-specific movement. Stay away from common rotator-cuff rotation exercises where your elbow is bent at 90 degrees and you rotate your hand outwards from your abdomen with resistance. Strengthen your shoulder, as shown in the photo on the next page, by holding your arms straight ahead above your shoulders and resisting against a band or strap.

6. Micro-Bend Your Elbows

Keeping a micro-bend in your elbows when climbing steep and overhanging terrain puts the weight into the skeleton and takes it out of the shoulders and biceps. The micro-bend should be so minimal that the elbow appears fully straight. This allows for greater circulation and more energy-efficient movement. Traditional exercises such as bicep curls are "old school" and reinforce a bad habit of bending the elbow. Instead, perform straight-arm raises with weights or bands.

The Perfect Climbing Exercise

This photo shows all six rules efficiently combined into a single exercise.

- Weight is in the toes
- Knees bent
- Abdominals engaged
- Shoulder blades engaged
- Hands above shoulder height
- Micro-bend in the elbows

Shoulder Blades Engaged

Hands Above Shoulder Height

Micro-Bend Elbows

Abdominals Engaged

Knees Bent

Weight is in the Toes

4. KEEP A STRONG CORE

The core-training concepts and content in this section were developed in collaboration with Steve Bechtel. Steve is a climber, trainer and strength and conditioning wizard who operates the webpage ClimbStrong.com.

Having a strong core allows you to apply forces in all directions. This gives you the ability to utilize available hand and foot holds more easily. Without a solid midsection, your climbing technique will start to break down and you may begin to develop overuse injuries.

It is important to train the core in sympathy with how it is used during climbing. The core muscles are rarely used to initiate movement but rather to control it. For example, it is uncommon to perform a sit-up or crunch while climbing. More often you use your core to maintain a tight midsection to prevent your hands and feet from cutting loose on holds. The core must be trained similar to how it is used when climbing.

Understand the Climber's Core
The climber's core involves the midsection, the shoulder blades and the hips. The midsection is made up of much more than just the abdominals. It also includes your oblique muscles on your side and your lumbar muscles in your low back. These muscles all work together as a unit to maintain tension throughout the midsection while climbing.

It is best to think of your core more like a wide stabilization belt that wraps around your body rather than just your abdominal muscles. This is why back braces are constructed to wrap around and support the spine as a cylinder. The shoulder blades and the hips are equally as important as your midsection because they provide the foundation for your moving limbs. The shoulder blades are the foundation for your shoulders, elbows, wrists and fingers while the hips are the foundation for your knees, ankles and toes. When the shoulder blades and hips are strong they can take the stress off the limbs while climbing.

Imagine Your Abs Are a Water Bottle
Take a water bottle that is a perfect cylinder and pour out one-third of the water. Press down on the bottle. You will notice that it is a challenge to compress the full cylinder. Now unscrew the cap, crimp the bottle and screw the cap back on. As you press back down on the bottle, you will notice that it deforms more easily.

Why does the cylindrical bottle maintain its shape while the crimped bottle compresses under pressure? The cylindrical water bottle is a structurally sound unit, like the cylinder of muscles around your midsection. If there is a weak link or crimp in the water bottle, such as a part of your midsection not working well, compression can occur. This is similar to having an inability to hold core tension while climbing. A weak cylindrical core can limit you from reaching that next hold and can potentially lead to injury.

The Four Core Categories
Core training is split into four categories which are depicted on the next page. The categories are: Trunk stability, trunk stability with arm movement, trunk stability with leg movement, trunk stability with arm and leg movement.

How to Train and Progress
You should train the core exercises on the next page 3 days per week. Select one exercise from each category and do it for 4 sets of 10 repetitions. Static holds such as Sideplanks and V-Sits can be held for sets of up to 30 seconds. If you can complete all the reps with perfect control and good form, advance to a more difficult variation of the exercise.

For example, let's say you can easily do a V-Sit or Sideplank for 30 seconds. What can you do to progress the exercise? Try lifting your top leg during a Sideplank or adding a weight to the hands and legs during a V-Sit. If you can perform 8 reps of a slow and controlled Plank Pull-Down with perfect form, increase the resistance of the band. If you have mastered 8 repetitions of Plank Knee Drives, progress the exercise by hanging from a bar and touching your knees to elbows. If the Double Knee Drive Press Down is no longer challenging, adjust your starting position by bringing the arms further overhead. The variations and progressions are endless.

The 4 Core Categories

1. Trunk Stability

V-Sit	Sideplank

2. Trunk Stability with Arm Movement

Plank Pull-Down Part 1	Plank Pull-Down Part 2

3. Trunk Stability with Leg Movement

Plank Knee Drive Part 1	Plank Knee Drive Part 2

4. Trunk Stability with Arm and Leg Movement

Double Knee Drive Press Down Part 1	Double Knee Drive Press Down Part 2

5. BE MINDFUL OF YOUR MOVEMENT

Remember back to when you first started climbing. Most of us just chalked up and learned as we went. Struggling and flailing up a route until either we found a strategy that worked or we got stronger. Contrast that to any other skill sport such as golf, tennis or gymnastics where movement is trained and refined by technique coaching on a regular basis.

Poor Climbing Movement: Excessive "Shoulder Shrug"

Climbing is a skill sport and proper movement patterns are essential to success. Unfortunately, the majority of climbers acquire skill and technique without formal instruction of safe and efficient movement patterns. The absence of a proper foundation of movement leaves you susceptible to overuse injuries and may limit your climbing ability.

Poor Climbing Movement: Excessive "Chicken Wing"

Correct Climbing Technique

Keep Good Posture

When your body is aligned with good posture the muscles can act more effectively and are less likely to strain. Climbing posture is similar to seated and standing posture. Keep your trunk upright, shoulders back and shoulder blades gently squeezed together. This will create a powerful foundation from which to move.

Bring Your Hips into the Wall

Your center of mass is a point around which the weight of your body is concentrated and upon which the force of gravity acts. That means, the closer your center of mass is to your toes, the less gravity acts on your shoulders, elbows and fingers. The way you move your center of mass closer over your toes (on steep or overhanging rock) is by bringing your entire pelvis towards the wall or by rotating one hip into the wall.

Don't Over-bend Your Arms

As humans evolved into upright creatures, we began to interact with our environments with straight legs and bent arms. This is why it seems unnatural for climbers to bend their knees and straighten their arms while climbing. However, when you bend your knees and straighten your arms, your weight transitions into your powerful legs where your body has the most strength. Try not to over-bend your arms while climbing, especially on overhangs. This means you might need to do a few extra foot moves, including getting your feet really high to stand up. This will reduce reliance on your biceps and forearms, while decreasing the chances of an elbow or shoulder injury.

Push with Your Feet

The muscles in your legs are the largest in the body. They are developed to support your full body weight. This is why they are so much bigger than your arms. When you push with your legs to move your body to the next hold you are moving more efficiently than pulling with your arms. Always think to first push with your legs then only pull with your arms if you have to.

Climb Like You Crawl

Babies learn early on the most efficient ways to maneuver in their environments. They learn how to crawl by moving, for example, their right arm first and then their opposite left leg, and then their left arm followed by their right leg. Climbing like a baby is the most efficient way to climb.

6. BALANCE YOUR MIND AND BODY

Understanding the Warning Signs Associated with Injury

When your mind and body are syncing everything comes naturally. When either one is off, it can be devastating. Imagine what would happen if you trained for climbing three hours a day and six days per week. You are going to burn out and likely injure yourself. Contrast that to another extreme. Imagine if you visualized climbing your project for three hours a day and six days a week while sitting on the couch eating potato chips. To climb at a high level it is extremely important to have a balance and to be aware of the warning signs that may affect your mind and body and lead to injury.

Listed below are the physical and mental warning signs that are associated with injury.

7 Mental Signs Associated with Injury
- Stress
- Sadness
- Change in Appetite
- Mental Lethargy
- Anxiety and Fear of Movement
- Isolation
- Decreased Focus

7 Physical Signs Associated with Injury and Over-training
- Physical Fatigue
- Difficulty Sleeping
- Excessive Swelling
- Joint Stiffness
- Muscle Soreness
- Skin Warmth or Redness
- Pain

Sports psychology, nutrition and in-depth training principals are outside the scope of this book. Here are a few recommended books that explore the topics in more detail: Training for Climbing by Eric Hörst, The Rock Warrior's Way by Arno Ilgner, Rock Climbing Nutrition by Aicacia Young, Paleo Comfort by Neely Quinn, Gimme Kraft by Patrick Matros and Dicki Korb, The Rock Climber's Training Manual by Mike and Mark Anderson. If you are interested in further understanding injuries and overuse syndromes in rock climbing, I recommend the book One Move Too Many by Volker Schöffl and Thomas Hochholzer.

The Teeter-Totter Theory

Your mind and body balance precariously on either end of a teeter totter. Giving too much attention to one leads to an imbalance. When the teeter totter is unbalanced you can slide off into an injury. Below are a few tips that can help you maintain your mind and body equilibrium.

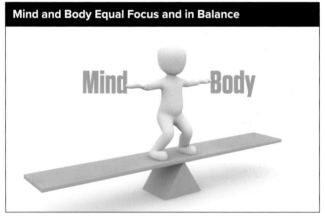

5 Simple Mind Tips
- Focus on the positive: Where focus goes, energy flows.
- Don't compare yourself to others: Everyone's physiology is different.
- Listen to your body: Learn your body's warning signs of overuse injury.
- Know when to stop: Don't climb through an injury.
- Have fun: The best climber is the one having the most fun.

5 Simple Body Tips
- Don't over-train: Learn your training capacity and don't surpass it.
- Get enough rest: At least 7-8 hours of sleep per night.
- "Eat food. Not too much. Mostly plants": A quote from Michael Pollan.
- Practice technique: Not all climbing training has to be on your project.
- Cross train: Different activities can prevent overuse injuries.

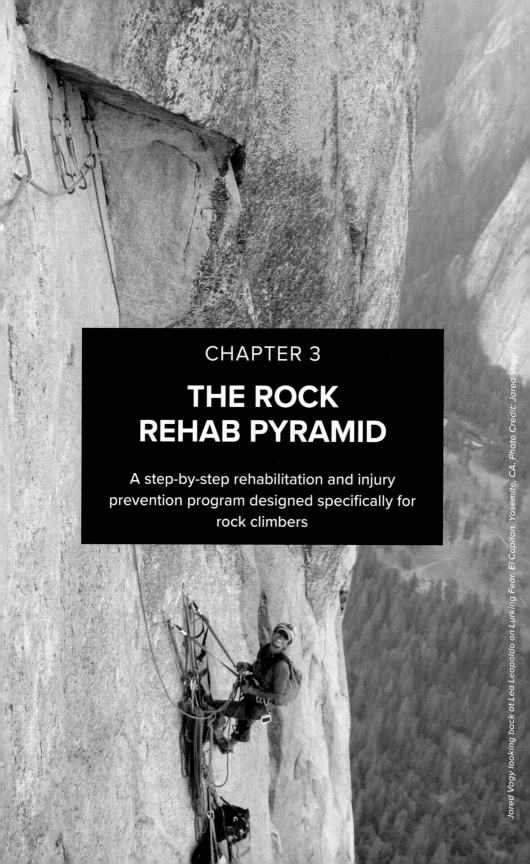

CHAPTER 3

THE ROCK
REHAB PYRAMID

A step-by-step rehabilitation and injury
prevention program designed specifically for
rock climbers

Jared Vagy looking back at Lea Leopoldo on Lurking Fear. El Capitan. Yosemite, CA. Photo Credit: Jared Vagy

THE ROCK REHAB PYRAMID

How to Use the Pyramid
The Rock Rehab Pyramid is a step-by-step rehabilitation and injury prevention program designed specifically for rock climbers. It is comprised of four phases.

1. **Pain, Inflammation and Tissue Overload**
2. **Mobility**
3. Strength
4. Movement

Most climbers begin the rehabilitation process at the bottom of the pyramid in the inflammation and tissue-overload phase. Through the rehabilitation process, you will progressively advance up the pyramid. The goal is to gain full mobility, strength and eventually pain-free climbing movement. At this point, you will achieve full recovery.

Perform Under the Guidance of a Medical Professional
The rehabilitation guidelines in this book are not a substitute for assessment and treatment by your medical professional. Perform at your own risk.

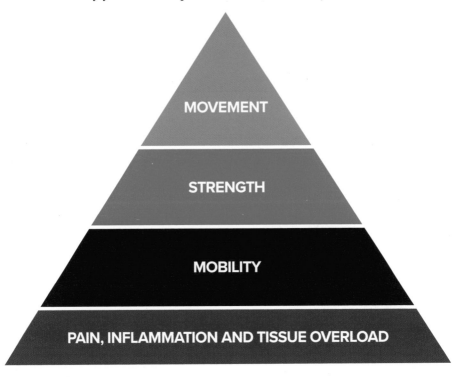

ROCK REHAB PYRAMID BREAKDOWN

Contents of the Pyramid

Phase 1 - Pain, Inflammation and Tissue Overload: Uses traction and taping techniques to unload the tissues. You can perform tissue unloading for as long as it takes for your pain at rest to subside.

Phase 2 - Mobility: Uses three progressive stretching exercises to improve range of motion. Each exercise can be performed up to three times per day.

Phase 3 - Strength: Uses three progressive resistive exercises to increase strength. Each exercise can be performed daily.

Phase 4 - Movement: Comprised of three movement advice tips and should be implemented during each session of climbing.

When to Progress to the Next Phase of the Pyramid

Once you are able to perform the prescribed exercises in a given phase of the pyramid without pain then you can progress to the next phase. Do not perform exercises if they are painful. There is no exact formula for how long it takes a climber to progress back to climbing and movement training. The recovery process is highly variable based on your injury and individual factors. If you have any questions regarding your progression, consult your medical professional.

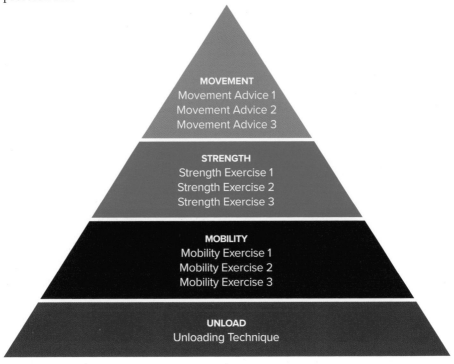

MOVEMENT
Movement Advice 1
Movement Advice 2
Movement Advice 3

STRENGTH
Strength Exercise 1
Strength Exercise 2
Strength Exercise 3

MOBILITY
Mobility Exercise 1
Mobility Exercise 2
Mobility Exercise 3

UNLOAD
Unloading Technique

1. Pain, Inflammation and Tissue Overload

This phase is at the base of the Rock Rehab Pyramid. It is typically the phase when you first realize you are injured. Oftentimes you will ignore the pain, inflammation and overuse until you can no longer climb. The longer you stay in this phase without addressing your injury, the further you will damage your tissues and the more challenging it becomes to fully recover.

1a. Pain

To learn how to reduce pain it is important to first understand what pain really is. Pain is an interpretation in the brain of a danger signal sent from the tissues in your body. Tissues in your body deliver signals to our brain along nerve fibers. There are three important nerve fibers in the pain cycle:

C Fibers: Small pain fibers that transmit slow burning pain.
A-delta Fibers: Large pain fibers that transmit intense pain.
A-beta Fibers: Ultra fast fibers that transmit touch, vibration and pressure.

All three of these nerve fibers carry messages from the tissues in our body into our spinal cord where the message is then transmitted up to the brain. The brain interprets the messages from A-delta and C fibers as pain and A-beta fibers as sensations. There are two common ways to reduce pain along this described pathway. One is to affect the signal as it travels from the tissue to the spinal cord, which is called the peripheral nervous system. The other is to affect the signal at the brain and spinal cord, which is called the central nervous system. Whichever pathway is chosen to reduce pain, make sure not to become too reliant on it. Pain occurs for a reason; to protect your body from injury. By blocking pain, you may actually be doing more harm than good.

Reducing Pain in the Peripheral Nervous System
A-delta and C fibers transmit pain sensations and A-beta fibers carry touch, vibration and pressure. Since A-beta nerve fibers are faster than A-delta and C fibers, they can actually block the transmission of pain to the spinal cord. The message of sensation beats the message of pain in the race to reach the spinal cord and the feeling of pain is replaced by a touch, vibration or pressure sensation.

Think about a time when you accidentally hit your elbow against a wall. What was the first thing that you reflexively did? Without even thinking, you likely rubbed your elbow. Rubbing the elbow stimulates fast-acting A-beta nerve fibers. Instead of feeling pain, it is likely that you feel the sensation of rubbing your elbow. However, this feeling is only active for as long as you rub your elbow. Once you stop, the pain comes back. This mechanism is referred to as the "gate theory" of pain because the fast acting A-beta fibers serve as a gate to block pain from entering the spinal cord. Although blocking pain using the "gate theory" does not heal or repair damaged tissue, it may be used to your advantage to break a constant pain cycle. Topical analgesics such as IceyHot®, Tiger Balm® and BioFreeze® are popular ways to stimulate A-beta fibers to block pain. Rubbing these analgesics on the skin creates an intense sensation to block the pain messages from reaching your brain.

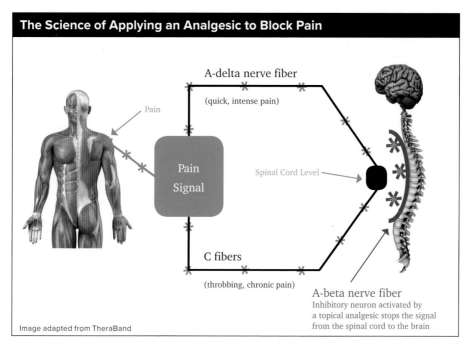

The Science of Applying an Analgesic to Block Pain

A-delta nerve fiber

(quick, intense pain)

Pain

Pain Signal

Spinal Cord Level

C fibers

(throbbing, chronic pain)

A-beta nerve fiber
Inhibitory neuron activated by a topical analgesic stops the signal from the spinal cord to the brain

Image adapted from TheraBand

Reducing Pain in the Central Nervous System

Although pain relievers such as Tylenol® (acetaminophen) have been around for a long time, the mechanism of how they block pain is still unknown. The most accepted theory is that pain relievers block the pain as it travels through the spinal cord and into the brain by altering the chemical signals that generate pain. This in effect raises the body's pain threshold. Acetaminophen does not have an anti-inflammatory effect, so it does not decrease inflammation. It only blocks pain. There are several additional medications that act as pain relievers. Consult your medical professional to determine which one is right for you. A complete description of these medications and their usage is outside my level of expertise and the scope of this book.

1b. Inflammation

The Roof Analogy

Imagine you live in a house with a roof made of wooden shingles. A tree falls and damages the roof. You decide to hire help to fix your roof and 100 workers come with buckets of clay. They arrive drunk and have no idea how to repair the roof. All they do is throw clay over the damaged areas. After a few weeks, they eventually leave and you are left with a functional roof but it is not as strong as it once was. This is how your body uses inflammation to repair damaged tissues. The process is messy and uncontrolled, but it gets the job done.

Inflammation Described

When bodily tissues are injured they often become swollen, warm, red and painful. This is inflammation, your body's natural way to heal tissues. When a tissue is injured a message is sent through the spinal cord to the brain. The brain recognizes the tissue is damaged and sends a signal back down the spinal cord to release chemicals to repair the tissue. The body does a poor job of regulating the number of repair cells and oftentimes sends too many. This is why the area becomes enlarged after an injury. The majority of the repair cells lie down scar tissue instead of muscle and tendon tissue to repair the damaged area. Scar tissue is made of different properties than the original tissue. It is weaker and is more prone to re-injury. This is why you are more susceptible to getting hurt again after an initial injury.

Reducing Inflammation Directly at the Tissue

Cold compression is one of the most effective ways to decrease inflammation from an injury. What is cold compression? It is just what it sounds like; a combination of cold with a compressive wrap. The combination of the two constricts blood vessels in the area where it is applied. It essentially squeezes out the inflammation through your veins. This allows the swelling to recirculate to your heart.

A few options for using cold include ice, cold packs or frozen peas. To compress the cold onto your injured site you can use an ace bandage, short stretch bandage or plastic wrap. If you elevate the injured tissue above the heart, it is even more effective to reduce inflammation. There should always be a barrier between the cold compress and the skin to prevent skin irritation. Typically icing times vary between 10 and 20 minutes depending on your circulation, body fat, depth and size of the injured tissue.

Reducing initial inflammation in this way allows for short-term improvements of increased range of motion and decreased pain.

Frozen vegetables or fruit can be used to ice painful areas of the body

Reducing Inflammation Throughout the Body

Medications such as non-steroidal anti-inflammatory drugs (NSAIDS) reduce inflammation throughout the body; not just in one place. They act at a chemical level blocking the creation of several enzymes that lead to the production of inflammation. Common over-the-counter medications are Aspirin, Ibuprofen and Naproxen. A complete description of these medications and their usage is outside my expertise and the scope of this book. It is recommended that you discuss the topic further with your medical professional or physician.

Whether or Not to Reduce Inflammation

There is a heavy debate in the medical community as well on whether or not to reduce inflammation. One side argues that reducing inflammation promotes a faster recovery by reducing pain, eliminating cellular waste and increasing overall circulation. The other side argues that reducing inflammation prevents our body from naturally healing tissues.

The Conclusion

There are many conflicting research studies and differing cultural opinions on whether or not to reduce inflammation. So what is best? The most accepted research conclusion is that short-term (less than two weeks) use of low-dose anti-inflammatory medications is acceptable in the treatment of sports injuries. However, long-term use of anti-inflammatories is not recommended.

If you are injured for several weeks and you are still using anti-inflammatories, it would be smart to reconsider. The best decision at that stage would be to see a medical professional to determine the cause of your pain and inflammation. It is possible that tight muscles, weak muscles or incorrect movement patterns can be leading to the continual re-inflammation of your injury.

1c. Tissue Overload

The goal of tissue unloading is to counteract the force that is causing the tissue overload. Whether the force is tension from tight muscles, weak muscles or poor movement patterns, the end goal of tissue unloading is to restore optimal alignment and body function.

There are several methods to unload tissues: Traction (1), joint reposition (2), structural support (3), tendon unloading (4), muscle off-load (5) and circulatory support (6). These methods are pictured and described on pages 60 to 62.

1. Traction
Traction is a method of spinal decompression by gently separating joint surfaces. The research on the long-term benefits of traction are poor but it can provide powerful short-term pain relief.

1

2-6. Taping
There are two primary forms of taping that will be discussed. Rigid strap taping and elastic kinesiology tape. Many of the taping techniques described in this book have been modified from their standard application and adapted to address the specific demands of climbing. Tape should be used conservatively and eventually discontinued so that the body can develop its own support instead of relying on the tape. Do not apply the tape over open wounds or fragile skin. Remove the tape if you experience discomfort, itchiness, skin irritation, numbness or tingling. When applying the tape, make sure to clean the skin well with soap and water. You can also use an alcohol solution. Taping is most effective over skin that is free of hair, so it may be necessary to shave the area before applying tape. Apply at least 30 minutes before climbing.

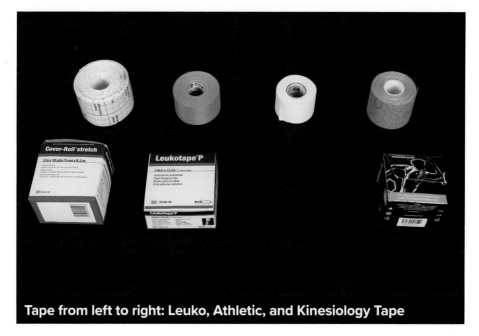

Tape from left to right: Leuko, Athletic, and Kinesiology Tape

Rigid Strap Tape

This tape is used for three methods in this book: Joint repositioning (2), structural support (3) and tendon unload (4). White athletic tape and leukotape are the two most common types of rigid strap tape. White athletic tape is more breathable but the effectiveness of the tape decreases after the first 20 minutes of physical activity. Leukotape lacks breathability and is more expensive than white athletic tape but it is much stronger. Leukotape maintains over 70% of its tension during athletic activities.

Leukotape should never be applied directly to the skin. When applying the leukotape, you must first apply a tape under-wrap called cover-role. This under-wrap protects your skin from the strong adhesive in leukotape.

Elastic Kinesiology Tape

This tape is used for two methods in this book: muscle off-load (5) and circulatory support (6). Elastic kinesiology tape has an elasticity of 140% allowing it to conform and move over the skin. The tape allows full freedom of movement and is excellent for increasing circulation.

Kinesiology taping techniques involve elongating the tape to different percentages of stretch. It is recommended to use TheraBand® kinesiology tape. This tape has indicators on the tape to help guide the proper tension.

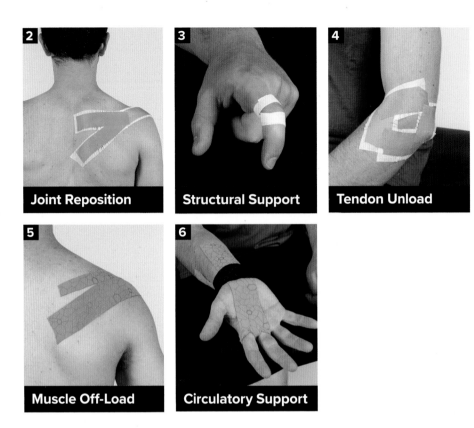

Joint Reposition **Structural Support** **Tendon Unload**

Muscle Off-Load **Circulatory Support**

2. Joint Repositioning with Rigid Strap Tape
The joint is placed in a stable and aligned position and secured with tape. The tape acts as your muscles to add stability and support.

3. Structural Support Rigid Strap Tape
The tape wraps around an injured structure in the body and acts to absorb tension instead of that structure.

4. Tendon Unload with Rigid Strap Tape
The tension in the muscle tissue adjacent to the injured tendon is absorbed by the tape and can decrease the pulling of the muscles on the tendon.

5. Muscle Off-Load with Kinesiology Tape
When the tape is applied with up to 25% stretch, it provides a proprioceptive stimulus through support and may off-load the muscle.

6. Circulatory Support with Kinesiology Tape
This technique reduces swelling and improves circulation.

2. Mobility

Over the past 10 years, abundant research has surfaced about the importance of moving injured tissues and not immobilizing them. The increased circulation, range of motion and muscle activity that is gained through movement can aid in the healing process.

This book follows an active rehabilitation approach that emphasizes using movement to heal. This is why there are no recommendations for immobilization devices in this book.

Movement, however, isn't the answer for some injuries. Examples of injuries that need immobilization are fractures, high-grade sprains/strains and dislocations. Always seek advice from your medical professional if you are unsure if it is safe for you to move and perform exercises in this phase.

Circulatory Massage
Increases blood flow to the injured area. It is most often used in body regions that are furthest from the heart including the forearm and fingers.

Soft Tissue Release
Releases adhesion within stiff muscles. It is most often used to break down adhesions within large overworked muscles.

Cross-Friction Massage
Breaks down misaligned scar tissue within the tendon to promote healing. The technique is performed directly over the injured tendon.

Stretch
Elongates the muscles to provide decreased resistance to movement. The technique can be static or dynamic based on the injury.

Tendon Glide
Glides tendons through their interfaces while applying minimal strain on the tendons. The technique is used for muscles and tendons that cross at least two joints in the body.

Assisted Range of Motion
Increases the range of motion of a joint with the assistance of an external tool such as a cordelette or dowel.

Circulatory Massage

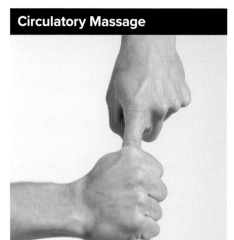

Soft Tissue Release

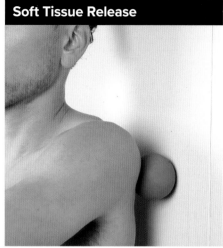

Cross-Friction Massage

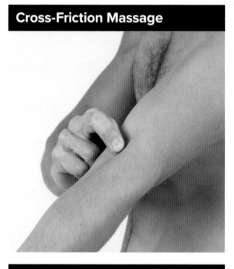

Stretch

Tendon Glide

Assisted Range of Motion

3. Strength

There are three primary types of muscle contraction: concentric, eccentric and isometric. These different muscle contractions are mentioned throughout the book. The examples below describe each muscle contraction in reference to the left triceps muscle in the back of the arm.

Concentric
The muscle shortens to create movement.
Example: Press a resistance band outwards with your triceps muscle.

Eccentric
The muscle lengthens to control movement.
Example: Slowly let your elbow bend back to the starting position.

Isometric
The muscle sustains a fixed position to stabilize movement.
Example: Maintain pressure outwards on a resistance band.

Using Muscle Actions Correctly

This book utilizes the three different muscle contractions for rehabilitative exercises. Each strength exercise in the book will clearly indicate in the instructions whether to perform concentrically, eccentrically or isometrically. The photos below show examples of each muscle contraction that are used in the book.

Concentric Letter L | **Eccentric FlexBar** | **Isometric Hang**

Progressive Loading

Each injury uses three strength exercises for rehabilitation. The strength exercises follow a progression of increased resistance. This means that each exercise is progressively more challenging than the previous. This allows you to improve the strength of your muscles in a stepwise manner. Do not progress to the next strength level until you can perform the exercise in the previous level without pain for the indicated sets and repetitions. You can progress to movement training and return to harder climbing once you are able to perform all exercises in the strength categories without pain.

Basic Exercise | **Progression of Exercise**

4. Movement

This is the most important rehabilitation phase. You can regain complete range of motion and full strength but if you return to climbing without changing poor movement patterns you are prone to re-injury.

Poor Movement Leads to Injury

Climbing technique involves repetitive movement patterns. Over time, repetitive movements can lead to wear and tear. Each injury covered in this book describes three common movements that when overused can cause wear and tear. For example, overusing underclings or sidepulls and climbing with bent elbows can increase the stress on the biceps muscle and tendon. If you straighten your elbows on overhanging routes, bring your hips forward during underclings and use the outside edge of the opposite foot during sidepulls, you can reduce the risk of developing biceps tendinopathy.

You will need to identify which of these movement patterns you routinely overuse while climbing and correct them. How do you know which movement patterns you are overusing? Set up your smart phone, tablet or camera and video your climbing technique. Have a movement specialist such as a doctor of physical therapy or a climbing coach analyze your movement patterns. When you review the climbing footage, you may be surprised at what you see.

Overly Bent Elbows

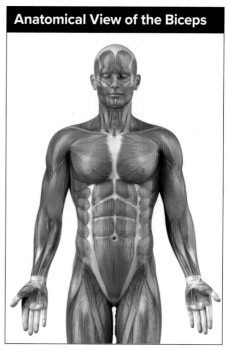

Anatomical View of the Biceps

Movement Tips

For each injury throughout the book, you'll find side-by-side images of incorrect and correct movement patterns. This allows you to easily visualize the necessary changes in body position. Making these changes in your own technique will not only help you climb injury-free but will also teach you how to climb more efficiently.

Change Your Movement to Reduce Injury

Once you have identified the poor movement patterns that may be leading to your overuse injury, you will need to change your climbing technique to reduce and avoid such injury.

Since it is not recommended to drastically change your movement patterns when you are climbing at your limit—this rarely translates into success—start gradually with technique changes. First implement the proper movements into your warm-up routes and then slowly progress to using correct movement patterns on harder routes.

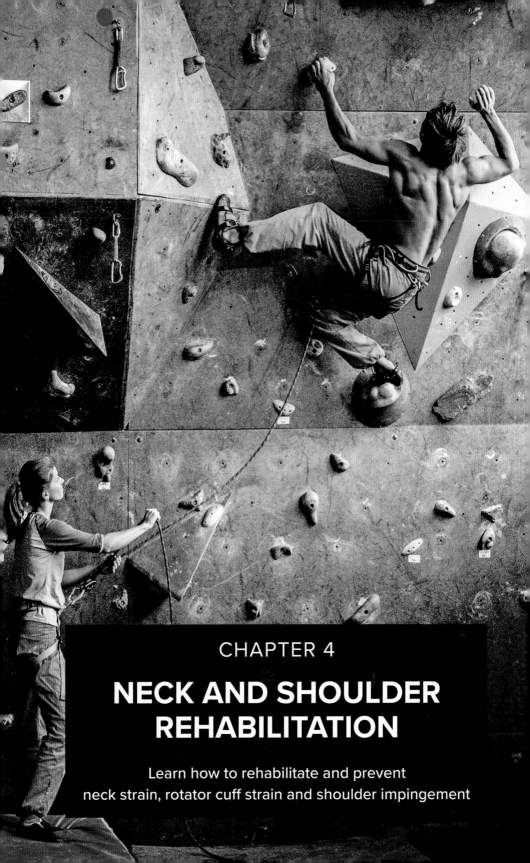

CHAPTER 4

NECK AND SHOULDER REHABILITATION

Learn how to rehabilitate and prevent
neck strain, rotator cuff strain and shoulder impingement

NECK STRAIN

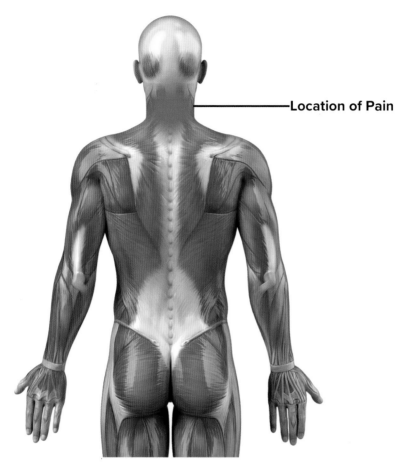

Location of Pain

Signs and Symptoms
- Pain, tenderness, muscle spasm or stiffness in the back of the neck
- Discomfort looking upwards or turning your head to the side

Cause
The neck is made up of flexor muscles in the front and extensor muscles in the back. When you look up at your partner while belaying or climbing, your neck extensors are constantly overworking. Over time, these muscles get strong and stiff while the neck flexors become weak, creating an imbalance. This imbalance can also lead to compression of the joints in your neck. You should be aware of the dangerous movements that can increase the stress on the neck and eventually lead to pain and injury. These movements are likely to occur from poor belaying postures such as a backwards-tilted neck, slumped spine and forward shoulders.

Unload the Tissues: Towel Traction

Instructions
Lie on your back with the edge of the towel hooked under the base of your skull. Scoot away from the door until you feel a gentle traction or lifting throughout your neck. Tuck your chin slightly towards the spine. The base of your skull should rest two fingers from the ground.

What It Does
Unloads and decompresses the joints in your neck by providing a gentle stretch and traction.

Frequency
5-10 minutes up to 3 times per day.

Advisory
Perform at your own risk. Set a timer for no longer than 10 minutes and make sure you do not fall asleep in this position. Maintaining this position for long durations can actually increase the strain on the neck. Make sure the knots are secure and the door is closed and locked. Perform with your head below a padded surface such as a carpet in case your head falls out of the towel.

How to Make a Towel Traction

What You Need
A bath towel, a piece of 5/8-inch tubular webbing or a cordelette and a door with a doorknob.

Construction
A Begin with a bath towel.
B Fold the width in half so that it is the width of your head.
C Fold the length in half so your head can fit inside.
D Secure the two ends with a cordelette to a door.

Tips
Make sure the towel fits over your head. Test the traction device by pulling vigorously on the towel to ensure the knot will not slip. Tie the opposite end of the cordelette to the doorknob with two overhand knots making sure the towel is hanging two fingers distance from the ground. Slowly lower your head into the towel. Make sure that the door is closed and locked.

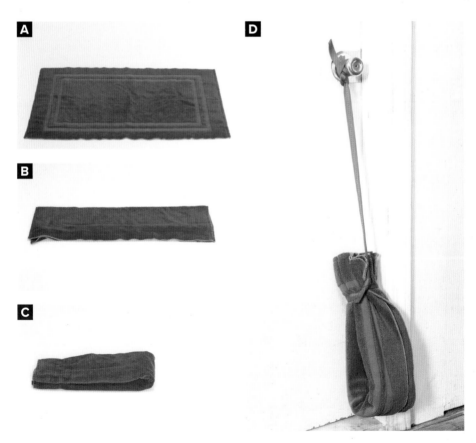

BEN RUECK
5.14 Trad Climber, 5.14 Sport Climber and 5.13 Big Wall Climber

I have learned over the years that having strong shoulders doesn't just mean having strong arms. It also includes strengthening the foundation of your shoulders, which are your shoulder blade muscles. Once I learned to engage these muscles, my training became a lot more effective. I wasn't hunching over as much and I began to stand up straighter. I'm not kidding, I gained a half an inch of height. Because I wasn't slouched anymore, my climbing improved. I learned to climb with the strong muscles in my back instead of just using my arms and became a stronger and more energy-efficient climber.

Ben Rueck on Pure Pressure, 5.14-. Escalante Canyon, Colorado. Photo Credit: Dan Holz

Mobility Level 1: Soft Tissue Release of the Neck

Instructions
Interlock your fingers and place your palms at the base of your neck. Squeeze your palms together until you feel a gentle pressure in the back of your neck. Continue to squeeze and release up and down the neck.

What It Does
Releases the muscles in the back of the neck that are put under tension while you are climbing and belaying.

Frequency
3-5 minutes up to 3 times per day.

Tips
You can tilt your head to each side while squeezing to increase the effectiveness of the tissue technique.

Mobility Level 2: Self-Fist Traction

Instructions
A Place an upside-down fist between the top of your breastbone and your chin. Take your opposite hand and grasp the base of your skull.

B Apply a gentle traction force, creating a fulcrum over your fist, pulling the back of your head upwards.

What It Does
Tractions the joints in the back of your neck using your fist as a fulcrum.

Frequency
3 sets of 30-second holds up to 3 times per day.

Tips
To get a good grasp of the base of your skull, wipe off any excess sweat from your hands and neck. If it is still a challenge to grip, you can place a patch of TheraBand the size of a sponge across your hand to increase the friction.

A

B

Mobility Level 3: Chin Tuck with Overpressure

Instructions
A Tip your nose downward slightly and retract your neck backwards.

B Apply gentle pressure downwards on your chin with your fingers to increase the chin tuck until a stretch is felt in the back of the neck.

What It Does
Stretches the muscles and joints in the back of your neck.

Frequency
3 sets of 30-second holds up to 3 times per day.

Tips
If it is a challenge to feel the stretch in the back of the neck, try rotating your head slightly to isolate one side. If it is still a challenge to feel a good stretch, you can firmly press and hold your thumb into the muscles at the base of your skull to manually release the soft tissue in the back of the neck.

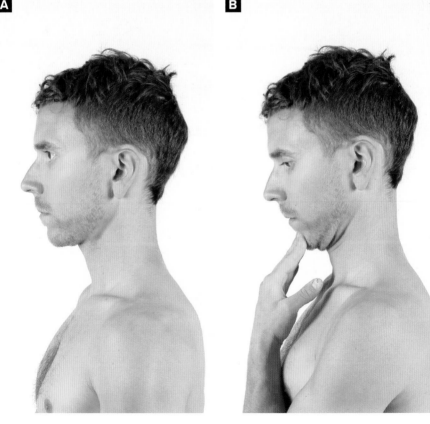

SEAN MCCOLL

**3-time Adult World Champion
and 5-time Junior World Champion**

I believe that being injured as an athlete and competitor is the worst thing. This is why it is so important to me to stay injury-free.

Traumatic injuries such as falls are difficult to prevent. However, most injures aren't traumatic and they build up over time. The warning signs of injury are rather apparent and it is important to be aware of them.

For example, midway through your session your tendons start to feel sore. This may be a warning sign for you to cut your training session short.

This is a hard concept for people who want to climb harder. People think that they have to feel pain and get tired from training. This is true, but there is a subtle line between training hard and getting injured.

Learning about your body over time will help you decide when to stop a training session early. This self-awareness is one of the most useful tools for climbers to prevent injury.

Sean McColl unlocking the sequence at the World Cup Finals. Vail, Colorado. Photo Credit: Eddie Fowke

Strength Level 1: Chin Tuck Against Gravity

Instructions
A Lie down on a firm surface with your knees bent.
B Tuck your chin and lift your head 2 inches off the surface.

What It Does
Isometrically strengthens the deep neck flexors in the front of your neck in a position against gravity.

Frequency
3 sets of 30-second holds once each day.

Strength Level 2: Helmet Press on the Wall

DIRTBAG TIPS
You can substitute the helmet for a folded pillow or towel.

Instructions
A Place your helmet on a wall at the level of your forehead. Stand upright with your forehead on the top of the helmet.
B Tuck your chin slightly downward and press your forehead into the helmet.

What It Does
Isometrically strengthens the deep neck flexors in the front of your neck in a standing position.

Frequency
3 sets of 30-second holds once each day.

Strength Level 3: Standing Band Belay

> **DIRTBAG TIPS**
> You can substitute the resistance band with tubular climbing webbing.

Instructions

A Stand upright in a belay stance. Loop a full body length TheraBand around the back of your head so that the ends meet in front of your head. Hold the tension of both straps with a straight arm directly in front of your head.

B Retract your neck so that your ear is aligned with the center of your shoulder. Use your free hand to grasp the excess band. Pull your arm down to a belay-brake position. Raise it back to its starting position keeping the chin tuck posture.

What It Does

Isometrically strengthens your deep neck flexors mirroring the same motion that you would use to belay.

Frequency

3 sets of 30-second holds once each day.

JONATHAN SIEGRIST
Multiple 5.15A Ascents and 5.14 Flashes, 196 5.14 Ascents, Several Big Walls up to 5.13+

I have been sport climbing for over 12 years. Throughout the years, repetitive belaying led to some stiffness in the back of my neck. I now use prism glasses while belaying and it has made a big difference in my neck stiffness. I no longer have to kink my neck back to give an attentive belay. I just stand tall with good posture and give an attentive belay without looking up. If you don't use prism glasses to belay, try standing further back from the wall when your partner is higher up on the route to minimize your neck strain. Or when your partner lowers down, have them yell "stop" at each quick draw that they are cleaning. This way you don't have to keep your neck kinked back watching them clean the entire route.

Jonathan Siegrist on Chronique Haine Ordinaire, 5.14b (8C). Ceuse, France. Photo Credit: Cameron Maier

Movement Re-education

Dangerous Movements	Correct Movements
Extending your neck back	Tilt chin down when looking up
Rounding your shoulders forward	Pull shoulders back
Slouching your mid-spine	Straighten your mid-spine

Movement Advice

Poor belaying postures repeated over time can lead to neck strain. The three characteristics that lead to poor posture are a backward tilted neck, slumped spine and forward shoulders. Imagine there is a plumb-line running from the center of your ear, through the middle of your shoulder and torso. When you become lazy whilst belaying you slump, causing your neck and shoulders to fall in front of the plumb-line. Try to be continually aware of these defects and correct them out of your posture as this will help to promote a proper belay position. Retract your neck back slightly to reduce the angle from your neck to your chin. Pull your shoulder blades back so that the center of your shoulder is aligned with the mid-line of your torso. Straighten your spine to avoid the climber hunch.

Poor belay posture

Improved belay posture

Wear Belay Glasses

Prism glasses can be worn while belaying to minimize strain throughout the neck. The glasses have mirrors built in that allow you to belay your partner without extending your neck back into dangerous and compressive positions.

Neck Creases Tell a Story

If you walk around and observe the back of the neck of your friends belaying at the crag, you will begin to notice some distinct differences. Some climbers will have significant creases at different levels in their neck and some will not. What are these creases and how do they form? The neck is made up of seven segments called vertebrae. During movement, the body takes the path of least resistance. Oftentimes when you look up, your neck will fulcrum at the most flexible vertebrae. Over time, this repeated motion can cause a default hinge point and a line across the neck. This is often the site of compression and pain in the neck.

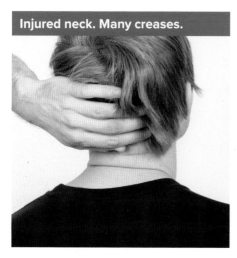

Injured neck. Many creases.

Healthy neck. No creases.

Rock Rehab Pyramid: Neck Strain

Below is the Rock Rehab Pyramid designed to rehabilitate and prevent a neck strain injury.

It is made up of four phases: unload, mobility, strength and movement. Begin at the bottom phase of the pyramid. Once you are able to perform all of the prescribed exercises in a given phase of the pyramid without pain then you can progress up the pyramid to the next phase.

Do not perform exercises if they are painful. There is no exact formula for how long it takes a climber to progress back to climbing. Injury recovery times are highly variable and based on individual factors.

If you have any questions regarding the prevention and rehabilitation exercises you should consult your medical professional.

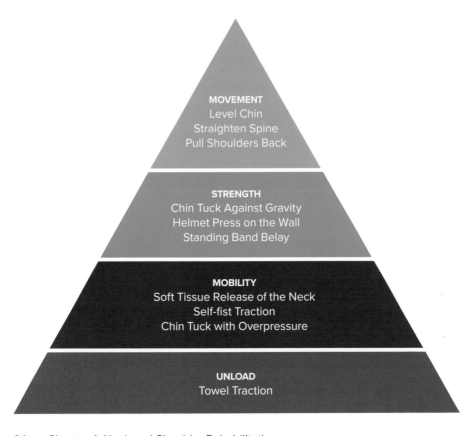

MOVEMENT
Level Chin
Straighten Spine
Pull Shoulders Back

STRENGTH
Chin Tuck Against Gravity
Helmet Press on the Wall
Standing Band Belay

MOBILITY
Soft Tissue Release of the Neck
Self-fist Traction
Chin Tuck with Overpressure

UNLOAD
Towel Traction

PAUL ROBINSON
World-Class Boulderer with Multiple V15 Ascents

Climbing isn't a sport you can force yourself into getting better at. I think a lot of people feel that more is better. Many people think if their climbing partner climbs five days a week and they climb seven days a week that they will get better faster. It just doesn't work that way. The small muscle fibers in our fingers don't develop that quickly and the technique comes slowly over time.

Understanding complex body positions and knowing how the body will move between holds has led to my greatest success on boulder problems. Climbing is so detailed in so many ways, the true way to improve your climbing is to focus on movement and technique training. What makes climbing so special to me is that it is not the strongest person or the one with the most endurance who can succeed. It's the one who understands their body perfectly who has the most success. This is something that develops over time and comes with practice. You need to accept that. If you can't accept that, climbing just isn't the sport for you.

Paul Robinson climbs Seeing Red. Driehoek, South Africa. Photo Credit: Alexandra Kahn

ROTATOR CUFF STRAIN

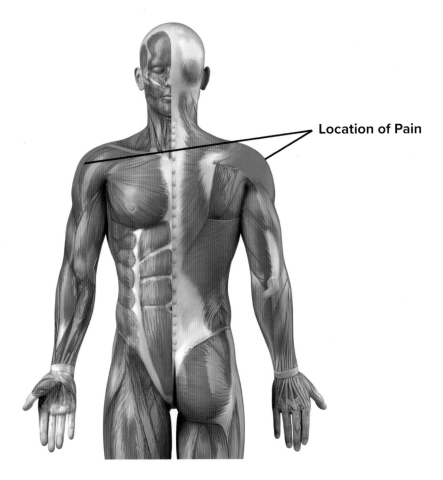

Location of Pain

Signs and Symptoms
- Dull ache radiating into the back or side of the shoulder.
- Discomfort lifting objects, especially out to the side.

Cause
The shoulder is made up of four rotator cuff muscles. These muscles connect the shoulder blade to the arm bone. The rotator cuff muscles act together as a unit to control shoulder motion. The rotator cuff is weaker than the large muscles that attach the shoulder blade bone to the spine. When you climb with poor posture and pull excessively with your arms instead of climbing with your shoulder blades engaged, you increase the strain on the rotator cuff muscles in your shoulder.

Unload the Tissues: Rotator Cuff Muscle Off-Load

How Long to Make the Tape

A Cut two strips of kinesiology tape with a sharp pair of scissors. To cut the appropriate size, measure the distance from the climber's shoulder blade to the front of their shoulder.

B Cut one of the strips of tape down the center creating two thin strips of tape. You will now have a total of three strips. One thick and two thin.

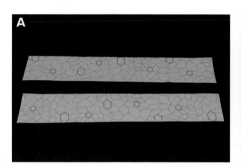
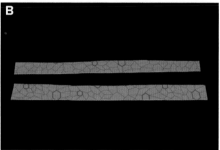

Taping Tips

This taping technique utilizes a specific amount of tape stretch to perform correctly, it is important to learn how to stretch the tape up to 25% of tension. It is recommended to use TheraBand kinesiology tape if it is your first time applying kinesiology tape. The tape has a hexagon box that transforms from a compressed box to a symmetrical box once 25% stretch of the tape is applied. If you are using a different brand of tape, please consult the manufacturers' instructions on use.

Stretching the Tape

C Holding the tape with no tension.

D Apply up to 25% tension. Notice how the small hexagon box (highlighted in red) becomes congruent.

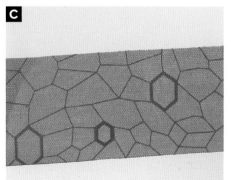
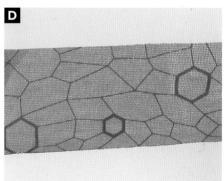

Instructions

A Begin seated with good posture with the hand behind the lower back. Anchor the tape to the front of the shoulder. Pull 25% of tension in the tape and secure the opposite end to the middle edge of the shoulder blade.

B Add a narrow strip of tape above the edge of the shoulder blade.

C Add a narrow strip of tape below the edge of the shoulder blade.

D Make sure the tape ends securely at the edge of the shoulder blade.

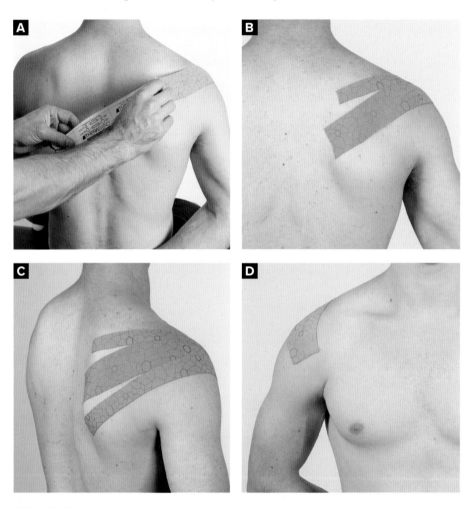

What It Does

The tape follows the path of your rotator cuff muscles in the back of your shoulder. This taping pattern off-loads the injured rotator cuff muscles to allow them to release and recover.

Frequency

Tape as needed. Apply 30 minutes prior to climbing. Remove after climbing.

ETHAN PRINGLE
**5.15B Sport Climber, Over 100 5.13/5.14 Onsights/Flashes
and V15 Boulderer**

I had a shoulder surgery, so it is important for me to do whatever it takes to continue to climb strong and pain-free. When I'm on the road or even just at home, I use a lacrosse ball to keep my muscle tissue and my fascia loose so it doesn't seize up when I'm climbing. I put the lacrosse ball against the wall and rub my shoulder against it. Sometimes I put two balls on either side of my spine and scoot up and down against the wall to loosen my mid-back. After this, I do a little yoga and some dynamic stretching to prepare for my climbs. This ritual has helped my shoulder significantly and I recently was able to climb 5.15b without pain, which is harder than I had climbed prior to my injury.

Ethan Pringle on Jumbo Love, 5.15b. Clark Mountain, California. Photo Credit: Anthony Lapomardo

Mobility Level 1: Tissue Release of the Rotator Cuff

Instructions
Place a firm ball against the wall or floor; a lacrosse ball works best. Lift your arm up and across your body to expose the rotator cuff muscles. Press your weight into the ball and move your body in a circular pattern. You should feel a point of maximal discomfort, this is most likely the stiffest region of the rotator cuff muscles and will need the most attention.

What It Does
When the rotator cuff overworks it becomes stiff and contracted. This can lead to taut muscle tissue which can restrict range of motion and lead to pain. The tissue needs to be massaged and released for the muscle to work optimally.

Frequency
8-10 minutes up to 3 times per day.

DIRTBAG TIPS
Anytime a ball is used for soft tissue release in this book, you can substitute it with using your fingers to self-massage. Tools such as a retired carabiner, soup can or even just a rounded rock are also good alternatives.

Mobility Level 2: Rotator Cuff Stretch

Instructions
Engage your shoulder blade back towards the mid-line of your spine. Use your opposite hand to press and fulcrum your arm towards your chest. A stretch should be felt on the outside of your shoulder. Make sure to keep your shoulder blade down and back when you are stretching the arm.

What It Does
Stretches the stiff rotator cuff muscles.

Frequency
3 sets of 30-second holds up to 3 times per day.

Mobility Level 3: Stick Press

Instructions

A Stand upright with a wooden dowel in your hand. A broomstick, trekking pole or stick clip all work well.

B Push your injured arm up overhead in a pain-free range.

What It Does

Increases the pain-free range of motion in your shoulder with the assistance of your opposite arm.

Frequency

3 sets of 10 repetitions up to 3 times per day.

Tips

To challenge yourself further try closing your eyes, performing a flag or balancing on one foot while performing the stick press.

MIKE ANDERSON

5.14 Climber and Developer of the Rock Prodigy Training Method

My philosophy on injuries is that if you're really pushing to be the best you can be you're always riding the razor's edge of getting hurt. You have to be hypersensitive to this. You have to listen to your body signals and know if you're doing too much or if you're not doing enough. This awareness develops over time by listening and learning about your own body. In addition to listening to your body, it is important to perform injury-prevention exercises and to use proper climbing technique to prevent injuries from occurring.

Mike Anderson on Scarface, 5.14a. Smith Rock, Oregon. Photo Credit: Janelle Anderson

Strength Level 1: Palm-up Band Reaches

Instructions
A Wrap a single resistance band around your wrists. Press your wrists outwards on the band while keeping your arms shoulder width apart.
B Reach up and out while rotating your palms upwards towards the sky and maintaining pressure on the band.

What It Does
Strengthens your rotator cuff muscles in a functional way that forces the muscle to contract together as a unit while moving the arms. This is far superior to isolated rotator cuff exercises such as the exercise where you stand and rotate your arm outwards against a resistance band.

Frequency
3 sets of 30-second reaches once per day.

Tips
Bend your knees deeper to more closely mirror the weight acceptance of your legs while climbing.

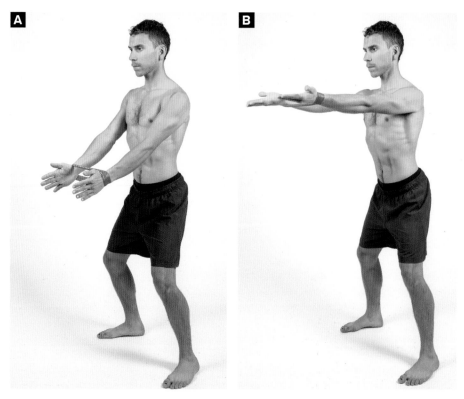

Strength Level 2: Air Clock

Instructions

A Wrap a single resistance band around your wrists. Imagine there is a clock in front of you with 12 o'clock at the top and 6 o'clock at the bottom. Press your wrists outwards into the band, keep your elbows straight and reach out towards various positions on the clock.

B Example of the left arm reaching to eleven o'clock.

C Example of the left arm reaching to seven o'clock.

What It Does

Strengthens the rotator cuff muscles by reaching the arms in different directions. This mirrors similar shoulder movements that are performed when rock climbing. Challenge yourself by performing air clocks on the rock wall.

Frequency

3 sets of 30-second holds once per day.

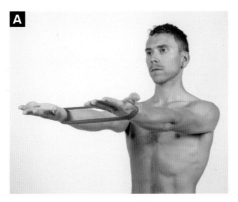

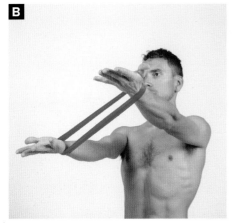

Strength Level 3: Kneeling Ground Clock

Instructions

A Kneel down and press your hands or fists into the ground. Wrap a single resistance band around your wrists. Imagine there is a clock in front of you with 12 o'clock at the top and 6 o'clock at the bottom. Press your wrists outwards into the band towards the positions on a clock.

B Example of the left arm reaching to 10 o'clock.

C Example of the right arm reaching to 1 o'clock.

What It Does

Strengthens your rotator cuff muscles as a unit and is a progression in difficulty from air clocks.

Frequency

3 sets of 6 repetitions to each number on the clock once per day.

MAYAN SMITH–GOBAT

Holds the Women's Speed Record on the Nose

Acquiring patience after my shoulder injury was the hardest lesson I have learned. After my surgery I had to be smarter about doing things right so that I would avoid re-injury in the future. I continue to remind myself of the importance of stretching, training oppositional muscle groups and paying careful attention to movement. I stretch with my foam roller. I strengthen with TheraBands and gymnastics rings. I know when to stop training and climbing when my form gets sloppy. I remember to take days off and focus on quality over quantity. I look at the big picture instead of being caught in the moment. Over time and disciplined physical therapy, I have returned back to the sport I love stronger than ever.

Mayan Smith-Gobat on Zappa, 5.13+ Escalante Canyon, Colorado. Photo Credit: Daniel Holz

Movement Re-education

Dangerous Movements	Correct Movements
Hanging on arms in rest stances	Engage shoulder blades
Climbing with poor posture	Maintain upright posture
Strenuous overhead reaching	Step feet higher

Movement Advice

Hanging on your arms during rest stances, climbing with a hunched posture, and strenuous overhead reaching can increase the likelihood of a rotator cuff strain. Proper posture is especially important during rest stances. It feels more relaxing to shake out your pump, rest and recover with slumped shoulders. However, this posture increases the passive strain on your connective tissue and can lead to injury. To avoid injury from resting or climbing with a hunched posture, engage your shoulder blades and straighten your spine. Strenuous overhead reaching is typically more common with shorter climbers. This can be avoided by looking for intermediate foot holds and stepping the feet up higher.

Slumped shoulder blades

Engaged shoulder blades

Rock Rehab Pyramid: Rotator Cuff Strain

Below is the Rock Rehab Pyramid designed to rehabilitate and prevent a rotator cuff strain.

It is made up of four phases: unload, mobility, strength and movement. Begin at the bottom phase of the pyramid. Once you are able to perform all of the prescribed exercises in a given phase of the pyramid without pain then you can progress up the pyramid to the next phase.

Do not perform exercises if they are painful. There is no exact formula for how long it takes a climber to progress back to climbing. Injury recovery times are highly variable and based on individual factors.

If you have any questions regarding the prevention and rehabilitation exercises you should consult your medical professional.

MOVEMENT
Upright Posture
Step Feet Higher
Engage Shoulder Blades

STRENGTH
Palm-up Band Reaches
Air Clock
Kneeling Ground Clock

MOBILITY
Soft Tissue Release of the Rotator Cuff
Rotator Cuff Stretch
Stick Press

UNLOAD
Rotator Cuff Muscle Off-load

SHOULDER IMPINGEMENT

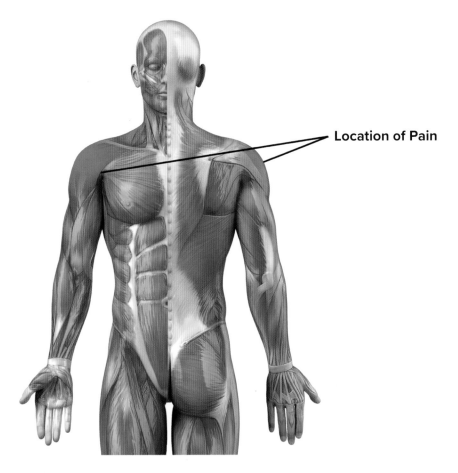

Location of Pain

Signs and Symptoms

- Dull ache in the front or side of the shoulder.
- Painful to lie on the shoulder.
- Discomfort lifting the arm, reaching across body and behind the back.

Cause

The tendons in the shoulder slide through a very narrow passageway and attach to the shoulder bone. Impingement occurs when the space between the bones in this passageway is reduced. This can occur from repetitively moving the shoulder into a stressful or suboptimal position. When this occurs, the bones in the shoulder pinch down on the tendons and cause shoulder impingement. Be aware of movements such as climbing with the elbow in a chicken wing position, mantling over the lip of a boulder and jamming cracks with the thumb down.

STEPH DAVIS
Rock Climber, Base Jumper, Wingsuit Flyer, Numerous First Ascents and Free Solos

A consistent pattern that I notice with injured climbers is they don't listen to their bodies. I've gone through this myself in years past when I was younger. There have been times when I have felt really worn out or tired. The fatigue can be mental or physical. Maybe you are really busy with school or work and you are stressed. Or maybe you are over-training and your body hasn't had the chance to recover. Sometimes we get this feeling that we have to push harder when we don't feel that good. It is at those times when you need to back up and check in with yourself. It is important to know when to push it and when you need to take it easy, basically just listening to yourself. Trying to push when you should be resting almost always leads to injury or lingering fatigue.

Steph Davis freeing the Tombstone. Moab, Utah. Photo Credit: Christine Bailey Speed

Unload the Tissues: Shoulder Blade Joint Reposition

Instructions

A Apply cover-roll to the front of the shoulder and wrap it down and around at a 45-degree angle until it reaches the center of the spine.

B Apply a second piece from the midpoint of the tape on the back of the spine towards the middle of the spine.

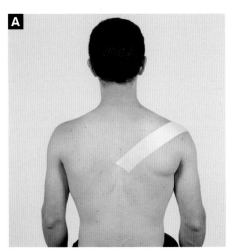

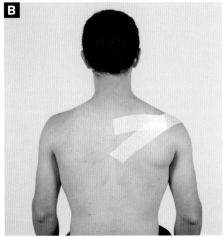

C The climber squeezes their shoulder blades together. Secure a strip of leukotape to the front of the shoulder along the cover-roll. Pull the tape taut and secure to the middle of the spine.

D Secure a strip of leukotape to the horizontal piece of cover-roll. Pull the tape taut and secure to the middle of the spine. Adjust the tension of the tape as necessary.

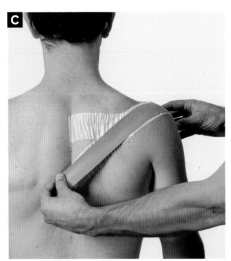

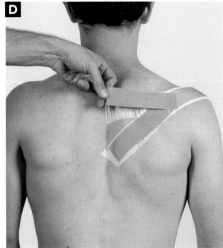

What It Does

The tape acts just as your muscle would to support the shoulder blade. Securing the shoulder blade in an optimal position allows for quicker healing, less pain and more effective activation of the rotator cuff muscles. The tension of the tape can be adjusted to provide more or less support.

Frequency

Tape as needed. The tape is very rigid and may limit range of motion while climbing. It is for this reason that it is recommended to wear during the day to unload the shoulder and not during climbing.

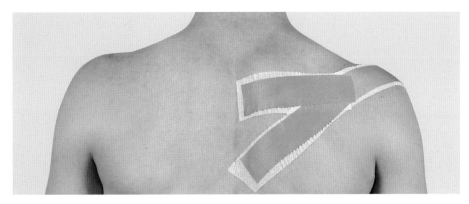

Wear a Posture Shirt

A great alternative to taping is wearing a posture shirt. These shirts are constructed in a way that supports the shoulder blades similar to the tape. The shirts are lightweight, breathable and easy to wear while climbing and belaying. They come in several different styles of support. My favorite brand is Intelliskin®. They do an excellent job with their products.

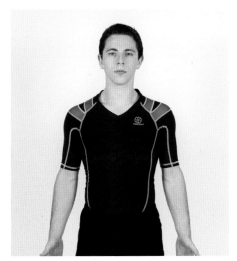

Mobility Level 1: Soft Tissue Release of the Pectoralis

Instructions

A Locate the collar bone at the base of your neck. Move your fingers slightly below the bone until you feel a stiff muscle. This is your pectoralis muscle. Rub in a circular motion applying as much pressure as necessary.

B To increase the pressure, you can use a retired carabiner.

C Put some lotion or sunscreen on your chest and massage deeply with the retired carabiner.

What It Does

Releases the tension in the pectoralis muscles in the front of your chest. Massaging this muscle helps you to pull your shoulder blades back more easily.

Frequency

8-10 minutes up to 3 times per day.

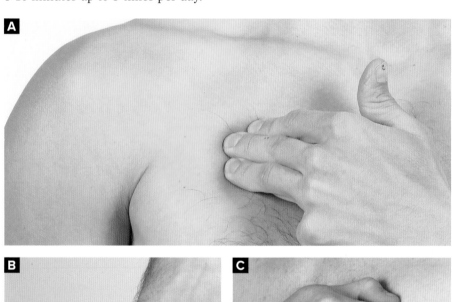

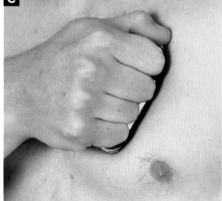

SASHA DIGIULIAN

First North American Woman to Climb 5.14D, Indoor Climbing Overall World Champion

It is important to have flexible chest and lat muscles for climbing. If these muscles are too tight, it will be more challenging to reach holds and it will be harder to keep your body close to the rock wall on reachy moves.

Tight chest muscles can also cause a "climber hunch." So remember to keep good posture when you sit, stand and climb. Stretch your chest muscles regularly in a door-frame or on a foam roll.

Sasha DiGiulian climbing at the Dardago sport crag in northern Italy. Photo Credit: Jensen Walker

Mobility Level 2: Pectoralis Stretch

Instructions
A Begin on your back with your knees bent and your arm out to the side. Place a heavy object such as a rock in your hand to increase the stretch.
B Engage your stomach muscles and rotate your knees to the opposite side.
C Begin on your back with your knees bent and your arm overhead. Place a heavy object such as a rock in your hand to increase the stretch.
D Engage your stomach muscles and rotate your knees to the opposite side.

What It Does
Increases the length of the pectoralis muscle for overhead and out to the side reaches when climbing. Stretching the pectoralis muscle will help make it easier for you to pull your shoulders back while climbing. The two different arm positions target the two different fiber orientations of the muscle. The arm to the side targets the clavicular fibers and the arm overhead targets the sternal fibers.

Frequency
3 sets of 30 seconds up to 3 times per day.

Mobility Level 3: Stick Press

See page 92 for a detailed description of the exercise.

Strength Level 1: Wall Angels

Instructions

A Stand against a wall with your feet 6 inches away and with your knees slightly bent. Tighten your stomach muscles so that your back flattens against the wall. Raise your arms to the side with the elbows at shoulder height. Either bend your elbows to 90 degrees or keep straight.

B Press your arms strongly into the wall and slide them up overhead while keeping your back flat.

What It Does

Strengthens your shoulder blade stabilizers to help prevent impingement. It is recommended to perform the exercise with both bent and extended elbows to train a broader spectrum of movements that are climbing related.

Frequency

3 sets of 8 repetitions once per day.

Form Tips

Squat down slightly:
Just enough to unlock your knees.

Engage your abdominals:
This provides a solid foundation.

Keep your sternum down:
Lower your breast bone.

Maintain a flat back:
Press your low back into the wall.

Press your wrists on the wall:
The back of the wrists should touch.

Tuck your chin:
Drop your nose down slightly.

Wall Angel with Bent Arms

Wall Angel with Straight Arms

CHRISTIAN CORE
Climbed the World's First Outdoor V16 and Indoor Bouldering World Champion

Getting injured is unfortunately a part of an athlete's life. We bring our bodies to the limit almost every day. It is important to be aware of all of the delicate parts that make up our body and to know that we can easily sustain an injury at any point. This forces us to be very careful, but sometimes caution and awareness may not be sufficient.

We can get injured in many different ways. A weight prolonged in time, a hold held in the wrong way, a hazardous movement or even a foot slip that unconsciously makes us crimp a hold with too much force are all common examples.

The important thing in the case of an injury is to deeply analyze the cause of it, try to understand the reason it occurred and how to avoid it next time. Correcting your movement patterns and performing injury-prevention exercises such as those described in this book can help tremendously with this.

Translated by Arianna Sanelli

Christian Core on La Mongolfiera first ascent, 8b. Varazze, Italy. Photo Credit: Stella Marchisio

Strength Level 2: Bent Over Letter T, Y and L

Instructions
Start position: Wrap a full-length resistance band around your torso (see page 112 for details how to wrap). Bend your knees and hips and lean your trunk forward to approximately 45 degrees. The closer to the floor that you can angle your trunk, the more challenging the exercise will be.

What It Does
Activates the middle trapezius (T), lower trapezius (Y) and the rotator cuff (L) muscles that provide support and protect your shoulder while climbing. The bent knee and forward trunk for position simulates more closely the body during overhang climbing.

Frequency
3 sets of 8 repetitions once per day.

> **DIRTBAG TIPS**
> Use a soup can, water bottle or free weights to perform the same exercise if you do not have access to a TheraBand.

Bent Over Letter T
A Start with the arms straight down by your side and palms rotated forward.
B Engage your shoulder blade muscles and bring your arms into the air to form the letter T. Make sure that the thumbs stay pointed into the air.

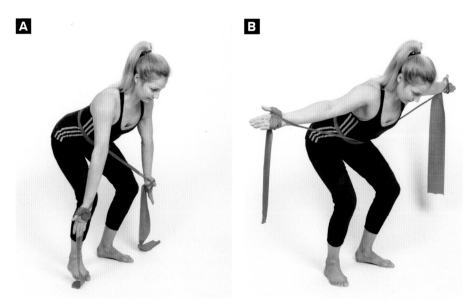

Bent Over Letter Y

A Start with the arms down by your side and palms rotated forward.

B Reach overhead with your thumbs up and our arms straight to form the letter Y. Engage your shoulder muscles throughout the motion.

Bent Over Letter L

A Start with your elbows bent at 90 degrees and raised to shoulder height. Rotate your palms down so that they are facing the ground.

B Rotate your hands and shoulder backwards forming the letter L with each arm. Make sure the shoulder rotates on a perfect axis and the elbow does not deviate up or down during the exercise. Engage your shoulder blade muscles throughout the motion.

How to Wrap the Band

This is the most effective way to wrap the resistance band to perform these exercises. The wrap around the stomach gives your abdominal muscles a cue to activate. It also alows you to move into climbing specific positions while performing the exercise. You can use free weights or cables instead of a resistance band.

A Hold a full length TheraBand in front of your stomach.

B Wrap the band around your back 1 to 2 times depending on the resistance you desire and the size of your midsection.

C Pull each end of the band in front of you to form a cross.

HAZEL FINDLAY
First British Woman to Climb a Trad Route at E9

I was climbing a route where I had limited footholds with several powerful and reachy moves. I am small in stature and very flexible but repeatedly doing the big moves was stressful on my body. Over the course of a few days of trying the route, I injured my shoulder.

I have always been very flexible. I believe one of the big reasons that my shoulder was susceptible to injury was that I had a lot of mobility but not necessarily the strength or stability at the extreme ranges of motion. Perhaps I may not have had my shoulder injury if I had known how to strengthen the correct muscles.

After the injury, I had several months of physical therapy. It was in therapy that I learned how to activate all of the smaller supporting muscles in the shoulder to balance the body. I learned that I had a weak lower trapezius muscle. I performed several exercises to strengthen it. I also learned several specific rotator cuff exercises with a TheraBand. These exercises have been effective in improving my shoulder health. The only reason I was able to climb for years after my injury was that I was constantly performing physical therapy exercises to strengthening everything around the injury.

Hazel Findlay flashes Masada, 29 (5.13a). Arapiles, Australia. Photo Credit: Adam Demmert

Strength Level 3: Inverted Shoulder Blade Squeeze

DIRTBAG TIPS
This exercise can also be performed on a rock wall. Find two large jugs on a 45-degree or more overhanging section of a climbing wall. The holds should be shoulder-width distance apart and will substitute for the rings.

Instructions
A Grasp two rings with your arms straight and knees bent.
B Engage your shoulder blade muscles and squeeze your shoulder blades together while keeping your arms straight and lifting your chest upwards.

What It Does
Engages the shoulder middle trapezius and rhomboid muscle that retracts the shoulder blades together. It also reinforces the movement pattern of pulling with your shoulder blades instead of your biceps.

Frequency
3 sets of 8 repetitions once per day.

Strength Level 3: Exercise Progression

Instructions

If you are looking to challenge yourself even more, try narrowing your base of support by moving your feet closer together. Or better yet, to decrease the stability in your legs, perform the exercise with only one foot contacting the ground. Placing the feet on a stable chair or bench can also add an additional level of difficulty to the exercise. The intensity of this exercise can furthermore be increased by using specific climbing grips to hold the rings, such as an open hand or half crimp grips.

Instructions for Progression

A Grasp one ring with your arm straight and knees bent. Reach your other arm back and behind you.

B Engage your shoulder blade muscles and squeeze your shoulder blades together, lifting your chest upwards while reaching with the opposing arm. Make sure to keep the arm holding the ring entirely straight during the exercise. Avoid bending the elbow to assist with Bending the elbow recruits the biceps muscles and decreases the effectiveness of the exercise.

Movement Re-education

Dangerous Movements	Correct Movements
Chicken wing	Angle elbow with hand
Mantling over a lip of a boulder	Utilize a pivot foot
Jam cracks thumb down	Jam cracks thumb up

Movement Advice

Climbing with the elbows above the shoulders in a chicken-wing position can lead to shoulder impingement. The alignment of the elbow depends on the angle of the wall. On an overhanging wall or roof, the most efficient position for the wrist and forearm is nearly perpendicular to the wall. On a vertical wall, the most efficient position is the elbow in line with the hand. This allows gravity to work with you, not against you. When performing a top-out on a boulder problem, it is often necessary to mantle over the lip. This is a stressful maneuver for the shoulder. When topping out, try swinging one foot over the lip on the low side of the boulder and using it to pivot your weight over the lip. This will take the weight out of your shoulder and into your legs. When jamming cracks always remember to utilize thumb-up jams where possible.

Chicken winged elbow position

Elbows angled into the wall

VASYA VOROTNIKOV
Sport Climbing Indoor National Champion

My shoulder injury snuck up on me. I was feeling my strongest ever and was climbing laps on this really strenuous boulder problem. I was performing this move where my whole body would rotate around my shoulder with my arm raised straight up. All of a sudden I felt a strong pain in my shoulder and I couldn't climb anymore.

I saw a surgeon and he told me that if I wanted to get back into climbing I needed to have surgery. He told me the best results are when people go to physical therapy for a month before the surgery. So I began physical therapy.

I performed different exercises with resistance bands to strengthen my rotator cuff and shoulder blade muscles. I learned to engage my shoulder blades while climbing instead of hanging my weight on my shoulder. Within a month I was basically pain-free and I canceled my surgery. I began slowly returning to climbing and within another month I was able to lead climb without a problem. All of the hard work rehabilitating my shoulder paid off and I ended up winning the sport climbing nationals that year.

Vasya Vorotnikov engaging his shoulder blade muscles while indoor climbing. Photo Credit: Jon D Petersen

Rock Rehab Pyramid: Shoulder Impingement

Below is the Rock Rehab Pyramid designed to rehabilitate and prevent a shoulder impingement injury.

It is made up of four phases: unload, mobility, strength and movement. Begin at the bottom phase of the pyramid. Once you are able to perform all of the prescribed exercises in a given phase of the pyramid without pain then you can progress up the pyramid to the next phase.

Do not perform exercises if they are painful. There is no exact formula for how long it takes a climber to progress back to climbing. Injury recovery times are highly variable and based on individual factors.

If you have any questions regarding the prevention and rehabilitation exercises you should consult your medical professional.

MOVEMENT
Pivot Foot
Thumb up Jam
Angle Elbows with Hand

STRENGTH
Wall Angel with Bent and Straight Arms
Bent Over T, Y and L
Inverted Shoulder Blade Squeeze

MOBILITY
Soft tissue Release of the Pectoralis
Pectoralis Stretch
Stick Press

UNLOAD
Shoulder Blade Joint Reposition

CHAPTER 5

ELBOW REHABILITATION

Learn how to rehabilitate and prevent biceps tendinopathy, triceps tendinopathy, lateral epicondylosis and medial epicondylosis

BICEPS TENDINOPATHY

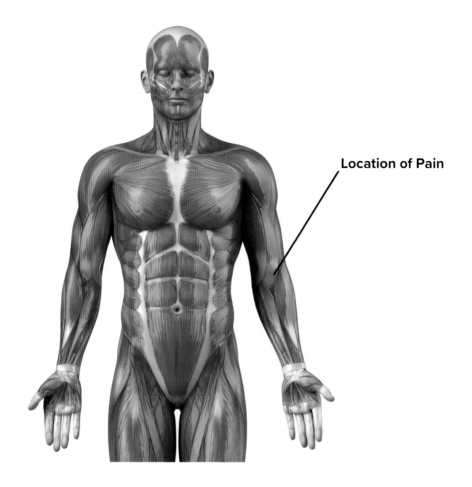

Location of Pain

Signs and Symptoms
- Pain over the biceps tendon towards the outside of the elbow crease
- Discomfort with actively bending the elbow
- Discomfort with passively straightening the elbow
- Pain with rotating the wrist outwards

Cause
The biceps muscle is a major muscle in the upper arm that flexes your elbow and rotates your lower arm. The repetitive action of constantly pulling while climbing can lead to degeneration of the biceps tendon as it inserts into the bone below your elbow. You should be aware of dangerous movements that can increase the stress on the biceps and eventually lead to pain and injury. Such movements include climbing with bent arms and straight legs and overusing underclings and sidepulls.

Mobility Level 1: Cross-Friction Massage Biceps Tendon

Instructions

A Cross your middle finger over your index finger.

B Expose the tendon of the biceps muscle at the elbow crease by gently resisting your arm into a biceps curl. Relax your arm straight. Place your fingers on the biceps tendon and apply a deep rhythmic force back and forth on the tendon with your crossed fingers.

What It Does

Cross-friction massage directed towards the tendon can break up scar tissue that causes pain and decreased muscular performance.

Frequency

15 minutes once per day.

Tips

Make sure your skin is free of any lotions or oils as this will decrease the effectiveness of the friction technique. It is normal during a therapy session for the pain to increase during the start of this technique. However, the pain should decrease after several minutes of performing the technique.

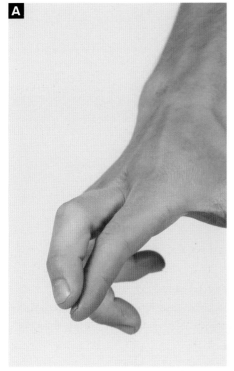
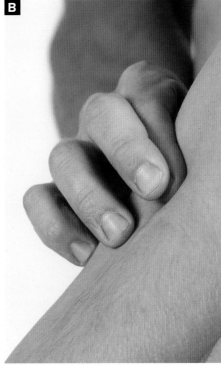

Mobility Level 2: Biceps Wall Stretch

Instructions
Stand one arm's length away from a wall with your inside foot stepped forward. Lift your arm to shoulder height and press your palm firmly against the wall with your thumb facing up. Contract your abdominal muscles, lower your chest and rotate your chest away from the wall. You should feel a stretch into your wrist, biceps and chest.

What It Does
Stretches your biceps muscle that often overworks and can become stiff from repetitive climbing.

Frequency
3 sets of 30 seconds up to 3 times per day.

Tips
Discontinue the stretch if you feel numbness and tingling in your hand. This stretch may put tension on the nerves in your arm.

Mobility Level 3: Backwards Palm Stretch

Instructions
Kneel on the ground. Rotate your fingers to face towards your knees and press the palms of your hands into the ground. Engage your triceps muscles to fully extend and straighten your elbows.

What It Does
Stretches your biceps muscles using the pressure of the ground. It is a progression of the biceps wall stretch.

Frequency
3 sets of 30 seconds up to 3 times per day.

Tips
Make sure that your elbows remain facing your knees throughout the stretch and do not rotate outwards. To achieve an even more effective stretch, gently rock your weight forward and pull your shoulder blades down and back.

Strength Level 1: Band Wall Slides

Instructions

A Wrap a full-length resistance band around your torso so that it makes a cross as seen on page 112. Stand 6 inches away from a wall with both elbows bent to 90 degrees and your little fingers resting against the wall.

B Press your little finger into the wall as you slide your hands upwards as your arms straighten overhead.

What It Does

Most biceps injuries occur from repetitive overuse of the muscle. This is why early training focuses on strengthening the antagonist muscle of the biceps, which is the triceps. This exercise trains a movement pattern that uses the triceps muscle instead of the biceps muscle during an overhead reach.

Frequency

3 sets of 10 repetitions once per day.

Tips

Lift your hands off the wall at the top of the motion to increase the intensity of the exercise and further recruit the shoulder blade muscles.

PAUL ROBINSON
World-Class Boulderer with Multiple V15 Ascents

Everyone has a different approach when it comes to improving their climbing. A lot of people train frequently on the hangboard, campus board and with weights. They say they are training to improve their ability to climb harder. But often they end up only improving their ability to train harder. I couldn't care less if I can perform 10 more pull-ups or hangboard on a smaller edge with 10 more pounds of weight. What is important to me is if I can improve my climbing technique on a boulder problem. Climbing is a movement-based sport and the greatest emphasis needs to be placed on skillful movement.

Paul Robinson on the first ascent of Long Way Gone. Zimbabwe, Africa. Photo Credit: Alexandra Kahn

Strength Level 2: Bent-Knee Airplanes

Instructions

A Begin on the ground on your hands and knees. Position your hands directly below your shoulders. Lift your knees slightly off the ground by transferring the weight into your toes.

B Engage your triceps muscles and reach one arm to the sky as you rotate your hips underneath you. Keep your abdominal muscles engaged and weight in your toes. Do not hyper-extend your weight-bearing elbow. Keep a small micro bend in the elbow to protect the joint.

What It Does

This exercise activates the triceps and shoulder blade muscles in a weight-bearing environment with body rotation. Maintaining a micro-bend in the weight-bearing elbow during the exercise forces the triceps to work harder than the biceps. This will help to reinforce a proper climbing movement patterns on the wall.

Frequency

3 sets of 10 repetitions once per day.

Strength Level 3: Row and Press

Instructions

A Begin in a plank position with a light weight in your hand. Position your feet as wide as necessary to improve your stability.

B Pull the weight towards your torso while maintaining a stable core and a micro-bend in your weight-bearing arm.

C Press the weight into the air.

What It Does

Activates the triceps and shoulder blade muscles in a weight-bearing environment with body rotation.

Frequency

3 sets of 10 repetitions once per day.

Movement Re-education

Dangerous Movements	Correct Movements
Climbing with your elbows bent	Straighten your arms
Underclings	Bring hips forward
Sidepulls	Use outside edge of opposite foot

Movement Advice

Climbing with bent arms and straight legs, underclings and sidepulls all place additional stress on the biceps. This increased stress over time can lead to a strain of the biceps tendon as it inserts into the bone. To avoid injury from climbing with bent elbows, transfer the weight into your shoulder blades and the powerful leg muscles. You can do so by straightening your arms, retracting your shoulder blades and bending your knees. When performing an undercling, remember to keep your hips pressed forward and the weight in your toes. If you are required to use a sidepull, make sure to put the weight into the outside edge of your opposite foot as this will balance the forces throughout your body more evenly.

Bent elbows: more biceps stress

Straight elbows: less biceps stress

Rock Rehab Pyramid for Biceps Tendinopathy

Below is the Rock Rehab Pyramid designed to rehabilitate and prevent a biceps tendinopathy injury.

It is made up of four phases: unload, mobility, strength and movement. Begin at the bottom phase of the pyramid. Once you are able to perform all of the prescribed exercises in a given phase of the pyramid without pain then you can progress up the pyramid to the next phase.

Do not perform exercises if they are painful. There is no exact formula for how long it takes a climber to progress back to climbing. Injury recovery times are highly variable and based on individual factors.

If you have any questions regarding the prevention and rehabilitation exercises you should consult your medical professional.

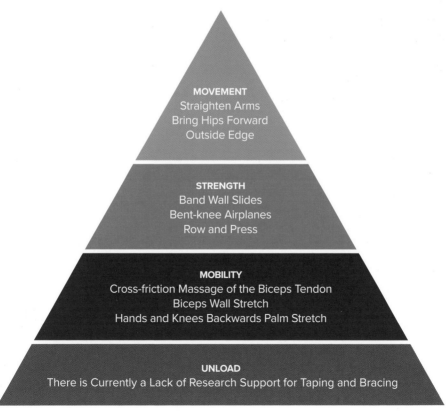

MOVEMENT
Straighten Arms
Bring Hips Forward
Outside Edge

STRENGTH
Band Wall Slides
Bent-knee Airplanes
Row and Press

MOBILITY
Cross-friction Massage of the Biceps Tendon
Biceps Wall Stretch
Hands and Knees Backwards Palm Stretch

UNLOAD
There is Currently a Lack of Research Support for Taping and Bracing

TRICEPS TENDINOPATHY

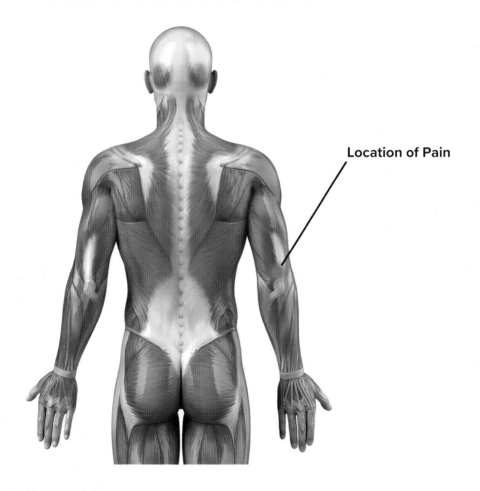

Location of Pain

Signs and Symptoms
- Pain in the back of the elbow directly above the bone
- Discomfort with actively straightening the elbow
- Discomfort with passively bending the elbow

Cause
When you climb, you are constantly pulling and overworking the biceps muscles in the front of your arms. Over time, the biceps muscles overdevelop and the opposing triceps muscles become weak, creating an imbalance. This imbalance can lead to overuse and micro-tears in the triceps muscle group. You should be aware of dangerous movements that can increase the stress on the triceps and eventually lead to pain and injury. These movements include the repetitive use of gastons, mantles, and the act of pulling a thick rope through a belay device.

SEAN MCCOLL

3-time Adult World Champion and 5-time Junior World Champion

One of the reasons why I have been able to stay injury-free over 100 world cup appearances is that I maintain a healthy body weight. My weight to height ratio (BMI) is higher than most of the professional climbers I compete against.

Many climbers restrict their diets in order to lose weight and improve their climbing. However, when you restrict calories, your body becomes more frail and is prone to injury. You need to eat food to fuel your body. You shouldn't just lose weight to get stronger. It is not sustainable. My diet is nothing secretive. I don't drink alcohol or soda pop and I don't eat processed foods. I prepare my own foods and eat plenty of fresh fruits, vegetables and protein.

Sean McColl eyeing his next hold at the World Cup Finals. Vail, Colorado. Photo Credit: Eddie Fowke

Mobility Level 1: Cross-Friction Massage Triceps Tendon

Instructions

A Cross your middle finger over your index finger.

B Expose the tendon of the triceps muscle. You can find the tendon directly above the outside of your elbow bone. Reach your hand across your body towards your opposite shoulder blade. Place your fingers on the triceps tendon and apply a deep rhythmic force back and forth on the tendon with your crossed fingers.

What It Does

Cross-friction massage directed towards the tendon can break up scar tissue that causes pain and decreased muscular performance.

Frequency

15 minutes once per day.

Tips

Make sure your skin is free of any lotions or oils as this will decrease the effectiveness of the friction technique.

Mobility Level 2: Cross-Body Cordelette Press

Instructions

A Measure the length of a cordelette from your shoulder to the opposite hand. Grasp the cordelette on each end. Raise both arms parallel to the ground with one elbow straight and the other bent.

B Gently pull your bent arm straight. This will bend the opposite arm. Repeat the motion side to side.

What It Does

Increases the flexibility of the triceps muscle and tendon. Improves pain-free range of motion of the elbow joint.

Frequency

3 sets of 10 repetitions up to 3 times per day.

Note

Vary the height and position of your arms to target different angles and ranges of motion. When changing arm position, make sure to adjust your arms symmetrically and coordinate equal resistance on each side.

Mobility Level 3: Wall Slide Arm Press

Instructions
A Stand 6 inches away from a wall with your arms straight overhead and your little finger contacting the wall.
B Press your little finger gently into the wall as you slide your hands downwards and your elbows bend.

What It Does
Eccentrically controls elbow motion. Increases the length in the triceps muscle and tendon while bending the elbow.

Frequency
3 sets of 10 repetitions up to 3 times per day.

Tips
Place a pair of socks over each hand. This will allow the motion to occur more smoothly. To increase the challenge of the exercise try staggering your feet in a stride stance and pushing your little finger more firmly into the wall as you lower your hands down.

A

B

Strength Level 1: Kneeling Triceps Extension

Instructions

A Start in a kneeling position on the ground. Wrap a resistance band around one hand. Reach your arm overhead and to the side. Grasp the opposite end of the band and straighten your arm.

B Slowly bend your lower elbow until your hand reaches your chest. Make sure to keep your lower arm aligned with your upper arm.

What It Does

Builds eccentric strength in the triceps muscle and tendon. The opposite arm reaching in the air mirrors reaching for a climbing hold while the bent-knee position with the hip forwards mirrors bringing your center of mass close to the climbing wall.

Frequency

3 sets of 10 repetitions once per day.

Tips

You can perform this exercise in a variety of different positions that mirror climbing movements.

Strength Level 2: Partial-Weight Chair Dip

Instructions

A Begin with your hips and knees bent and your palms resting on the front of a secure chair or bench.

B Pull your shoulder blades back and slowly lower down so that your elbows are at a 90-degree angle. Make sure to keep your elbows tucked in closely to your torso and prevent your shoulders from rolling forward. Use your legs to stand up, reposition your body back into the starting position and lower your body back down.

What It Does

Builds eccentric strength in the triceps while weight bearing.

Frequency

3 sets of 10 repetitions once per day.

Tips

This exercise is beneficial to eccentrically load the triceps. However, it also stresses the front of the shoulder. Do not perform this exercise if you have shoulder pain. If you have a second chair, it is best to perform this exercise with one chair on each side of the body. This way the center of body gravity remains all the time between the points of contact of the hands.

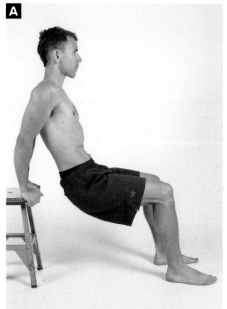 

JONATHAN SIEGRIST

Multiple 5.15A Ascents and 5.14 Flashes, 196 5.14 Ascents and Several Big Walls Up to 5.13+

One of the keys to preventing back-of-the-elbow pain is to keep your triceps muscles strong and to avoid prolonged awkward elbow positions. Performing bodyweight dips and using resistance bands can help strengthen these muscles. Always remember to keep your shoulder blades engaged when performing these exercises to provide a stable foundation for your triceps muscles.

Jonathan Siegrist attempts Victims del Passat, 5.14c (8c+). Catalunya, Spain. Photo Credit: Cameron Maier

Strength Level 3: Bear Eccentric Triceps Push-up

Instructions

A Begin on the ground on your hands and knees. Position your hands directly below your shoulders with your arms straight. Lift your knees slightly off the ground by transferring the weight into your toes.

B Lower your body by slowly bending your elbows.

C Once your knees touch the ground, rest the weight into your legs and straighten your elbows by rocking your weight backwards.

D Rock forward with straight arms and prepare to begin the exercise again.

What It Does

Builds eccentric strength in the triceps muscle and tendon while in a weight bearing position.

Frequency

3 sets of 10 repetitions once per day.

Movement Re-education

Dangerous Movements	Correct Movements
Gaston	Use inside edge of opposite foot
Mantle	Push with your legs
Belaying with a thick rope	Use a thin rope or lead climb

Movement Advice

Typically, when climbers use their triceps muscles, the elbow joint is often placed in awkward and suboptimal positions. The repetitive use of gastons and mantles combined with the act of pulling a thick rope through a belay device can all lead to increased strain on the triceps tendon. To avoid strain of the triceps during a gaston, place more weight into the inside edge of your opposite foot. When performing a mantle always remember to use your lower body to generate additional power to take the strain off the triceps muscles. If you are belaying with a thick rope, you may need to change to a thinner rope. Either shell out the cash to buy a thinner rope or stay on the sharp end and rope-gun your partners up single pitch routes, thus eliminating the need for you to belay.

Gaston: more stress

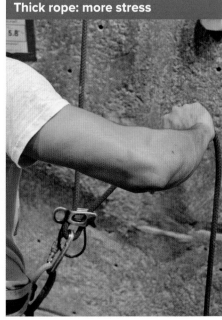

Thick rope: more stress

Rock Rehab Pyramid: Triceps Tendinopathy

Below is the Rock Rehab Pyramid designed to rehabilitate and prevent a triceps tendinopathy injury.

It is made up of four phases: unload, mobility, strength and movement. Begin at the bottom phase of the pyramid. Once you are able to perform all of the prescribed exercises in a given phase of the pyramid without pain then you can progress up the pyramid to the next phase.

Do not perform exercises if they are painful. There is no exact formula for how long it takes a climber to progress back to climbing. Injury recovery times are highly variable and based on individual factors.

If you have any questions regarding the prevention and rehabilitation exercises you should consult your medical professional.

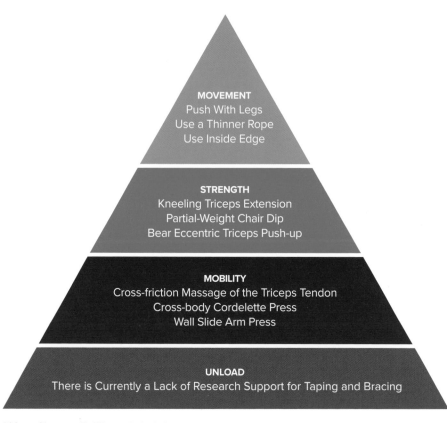

MOVEMENT
Push With Legs
Use a Thinner Rope
Use Inside Edge

STRENGTH
Kneeling Triceps Extension
Partial-Weight Chair Dip
Bear Eccentric Triceps Push-up

MOBILITY
Cross-friction Massage of the Triceps Tendon
Cross-body Cordelette Press
Wall Slide Arm Press

UNLOAD
There is Currently a Lack of Research Support for Taping and Bracing

LATERAL EPICONDYLOSIS

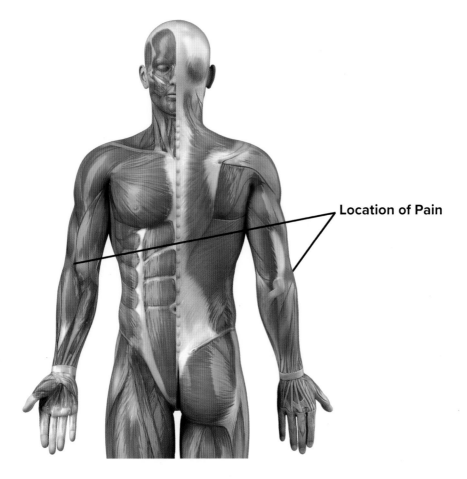

Location of Pain

Signs and Symptoms
- Painful localized point along the outside of the forearm
- Discomfort with actively extending the wrist backwards
- Discomfort with passively flexing the wrist forward

Cause
When you climb, you are constantly overworking the finger and wrist flexors in the front of your forearm by gripping. However, every time that you grip a hold, the muscles in the back of your forearm contract to stabilize the wrist. This constant activation of the muscles in the back of your forearm can lead to overuse and injury at the origin of the muscle on the outside of the elbow called the lateral epicondyle. You should be aware of dangerous movements that can lead to injury. This includes gripping with an extended wrist, climbing with your elbows away from the wall and jamming wide cracks.

Unloading: Lateral Epicondyle Tendon Unload

Instructions
Find your lateral epicondyle, which is the knobby bone on the outside of your elbow. Cut four strips of rigid strap tape into 8-10 cm pieces. Flex your elbow to 20 degrees.

A, B, C, D   Apply the cover-role in a diamond shaped pattern around the lateral epicondyle of the elbow.

E, F, G, H, I   Place the leukotape on top of the cover-role. Secure one end down by pressing firmly. Pull the other end towards the elbow with the desired tension.

What It Does
Research has shown that this taping technique can decrease pain and increase strength. The tape puts the tendon on slack by taking up the tension in the soft tissue surrounding it.

Frequency
Tape as needed. The tape is very rigid and may limit range of motion while climbing. It is for this reason that it is recommended to wear during the day to unload the elbow and not during climbing.

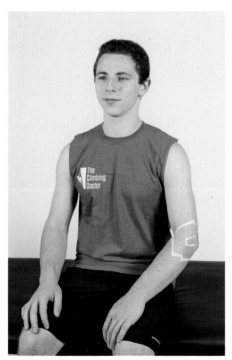
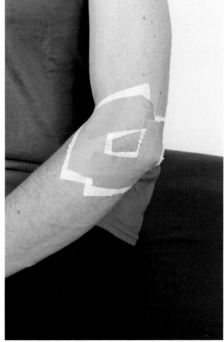

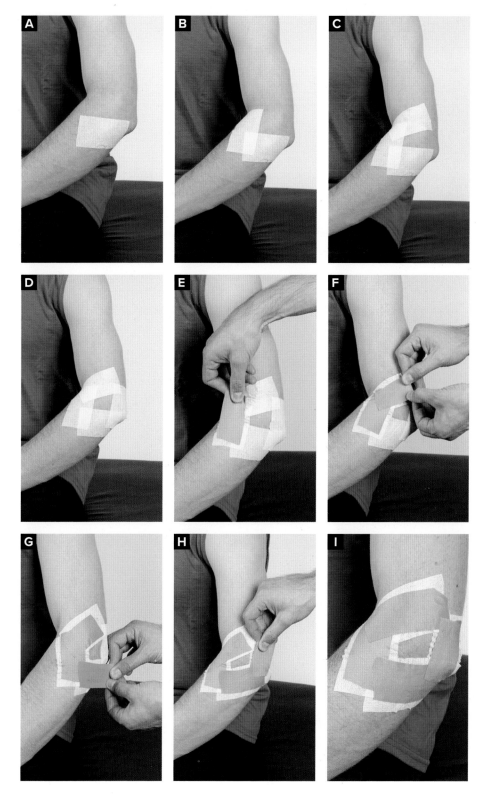

Mobility Level 1: Soft Tissue Release of Wrist Extensors

> **DIRTBAG TIPS**
> You can use your hand, lacrosse ball, soup can or a specialized device such as an Armaid to perform soft tissue release of your muscles.

Instructions

A Target your outside forearm muscles by finding the tightest location along the muscle. Extend your wrist and clamp down on the device.

B Keep pressure on the device and straighten your wrist to neutral to create an active release of the soft tissue.

C You can also perform using a lacrosse ball or soup can.

What It Does

Releases the tension in the wrist extensor muscles in the back of your forearm. Massaging this muscle reduces the stress on the tendon. Stop immediately if you feel any numbness, pins and needles, or a sense of weakness further down the arm.

Frequency

8-10 minutes up to 3 times per day.

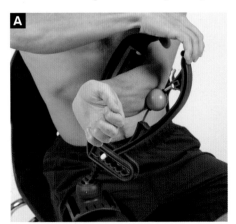

CHRISTIAN CORE
Climbed the World's First Outdoor V16 and Indoor Bouldering World Champion

Climbing makes us feel alive. We dedicate our lives to a passion. We are present in what we do, because it is a part of us. It allows us to sustain for long periods of time under strenuous workloads. It helps us continue to believe in ourselves even when we get hurt. It allows us to travel the world and share incredible moments. It ignites a flame inside. Feed this internal flame, because it will be your force to climb strong and stay injury-free.

Translated by Arianna Sanelli

Christian Core on Giada, V11 (8a). Australia. Photo Credit: Stella Marchisio

Mobility Level 2: Elbow and Wrist Tendon Glides

Instructions

A Begin with your elbows bent and wrists flexed.

B Extend your elbows and wrists simultaneously.

C Begin with your elbows bent and wrists flexed.

D Perform the tendon glides at varying angles or in a similar sequence to the moves on your climbing project.

What It Does

In the starting position it lengthens the tendons at the wrist and shortens the tendons at the elbow. In the finishing position it does the reverse. This allows the tendon to glide safely and therapeutically without increasing stress.

Frequency

3 sets of 10 repetitions up to 3 times per day.

Mobility Level 3: Paint the Wall

Instructions

A Stand one arm's length away from a wall with your hand at shoulder height and your palm pressed into the wall. Slide your arm down the wall as you press.

B Reverse the hand position and press the back of your hand into the wall. Slide your arm up the wall as you press.

What It Does

Provides a dynamic stretch to the muscles and tendons in the front and back of the forearm and wrist. Pressing into the wall activates the same muscles that are being stretched. This combination of stretching with muscle action provides the most effective form of mobilization.

Frequency

3 sets of 10 repetitions up to 3 times per day.

Note

It is recommended to place a pair of socks over each hand while performing the exercise. This will allow the motion to occur more smoothly.

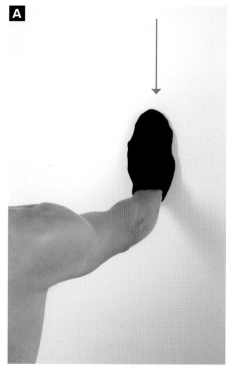
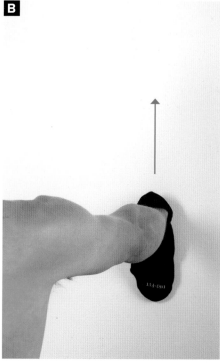

SASHA DIGIULIAN

First North American Woman to Climb 5.14D and Indoor Climbing Overall World Champion

It is no fun having an injury. It is often mentally, physically and emotionally draining. So I do everything that I can to stop injuries from happening in the first place. Here are a few tips that have helped me prevent injuries.

Warm-up: A thorough warm-up is really important not only before I climb but also before I train. I will start my warm-up with some light aerobic exercises or by rowing on an erg machine. This helps increase my heart rate and blood flow. I then follow-up with dynamic stretching. I listen to upbeat music like hip-hop during my warm-up and training routine. The music helps get me into a rhythm and keeps my mood and energy high.

Self Massage: I always travel with a foam roller. They are amazing! There are certain muscles that get stiff on my body so I use the roller to get the knots out. I also use an Orb ball and a lacrosse ball to self massage tight muscles. I focus on my mid-back, chest, the lats and leg muscles.

Train Oppositional Muscles: I use TheraBands to perform corrective exercises. They are portable, versatile and are easy to use. I target my rotator cuff and shoulder blade muscles. Strengthening these muscles helps improve my posture and keeps my shoulders from caving forward.

Diversify: Climbing has the potential of being a year-round sport. There is always good weather to find during the year. Though, I cannot think of any other sport in which athletes are expected to peak perform at all times during the year. So for climbing, in order to keep a healthy routine, maximize psyche, and remain non-injured, I think that it is really important to take rest periods; also known as, an off-season.

Stop When It Hurts: When my body is feeling tired and tweaky, I will take the day off training. It is not worth it to me to train through pain. I would just end up getting hurt. Stopping when you just aren't feeling it and resting is just as important as physical training. The body needs the time to recover.

Climb with Proper Technique: Climbing with proper technique is essential to preventing overuse injuries. Over the years I have learned how to change my movement to limit the stress on my body while climbing. A few key movement tips are to avoid chicken wings by keeping the elbows angled slightly downward, engage the shoulder blades while making strenuous moves, keep the arms straight and legs bent to increase climbing efficiency and limit using slanted far-too-reach pockets that may tweak the wrist and fingers.

Sasha DiGiulian on La Chirurgien Du Crepuscule 5.13d (8b). Ceuse, France. Photo Credit: Jensen Walker

Strength Level 1: FlexBar Eccentric Twists

Instructions

A Hold the FlexBar in your painful hand with your wrist extended back.

B Grasp the other end of the rubber bar with the non-painful hand.

C Twist the bar by flexing the non-painful wrist while holding the painful wrist in back in extension.

D Bring your arms in front of your body with your elbows straight maintaining the twist in the bar.

E Slowly untwist the bar by allowing the painful wrist to flex forward.

What It Does

This exercise targets the wrist extensors that insert into your lateral epicondyle with an eccentric exercise. Research has shown that eccentric exercises can strengthen the tendon and decrease pain.

Frequency

3 sets of 15 repetitions up to 3 times per day.

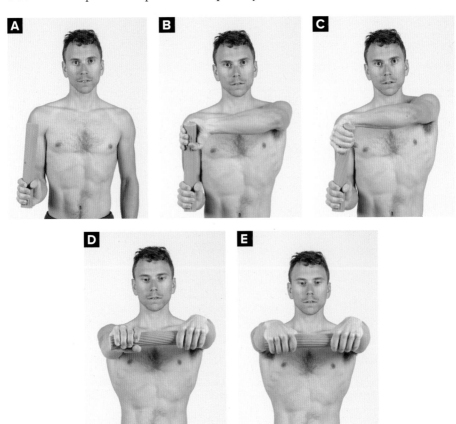

Strength Level 2: Weighted Dowel Lowers

DIRTBAG TIPS
Refer to page 152 to learn how to construct your own weighted dowel out of household equipment.

Instructions
A Hold the dowel with straight arms at shoulders height in front of you. Make sure that the weight is wound up fully and touching the dowel.

B Slowly alternate flexing your wrists forward to lower the weight until it reaches the ground. Place the dowel on the ground to make it easier to wind back up. Wind the cordelette up until the weight touches the dowel. Stand back up and return to your starting position. Repeat lowering the weight with your arms straight in front of you.

What It Does
Targets the wrist extensors eccentrically to strengthen the tendon that attaches to your lateral epicondyle.

Frequency
3 sets until fatigued once per day.

Dowel Construction

Build your own piece of exercise equipment at home.

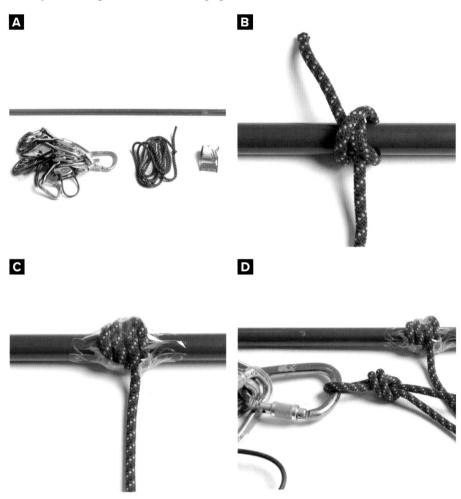

What You Need

- Broom or dowel
- 6-7 feet of climbing cordelette
- Tape
- 2-3 pound weight, a set of quickdraws or your trad rack

Construction

A Take a small dowel such as a broom stick or pvc pipe.
B Tie a clove hitch to secure the cordelette to the center of the dowel.
C Tape the knot securely.
D Tie a figure 8 on a bight on the other end of the webbing and attach your desired weight with a locking carabiner.

Strength Level 3: Concentric and Eccentric Twists

DIRTBAG TIPS
If you don't have a FlexBar you don't have to worry. You can use a rolled up bath towel instead to perform this exercise.

Instructions

A Hold the FlexBar with both hands at shoulder height in front of you. Stabilize the FlexBar with the muscles in your wrist and don't let it twist.

B Bend your painful wrist backwards and then return to the start position.

C You can also perform with a light weight. Bend your wrist forward.

D Slowly bend your wrist backwards. Make sure to slowly lower the weight forwards so as to exaggerate the eccentric component of the exercise.

What It Does

Targets the wrist extensors both concentrically and eccentrically to strengthen the tendon that attaches to your lateral epicondyle.

Frequency

3 sets of 15 repetitions once per day.

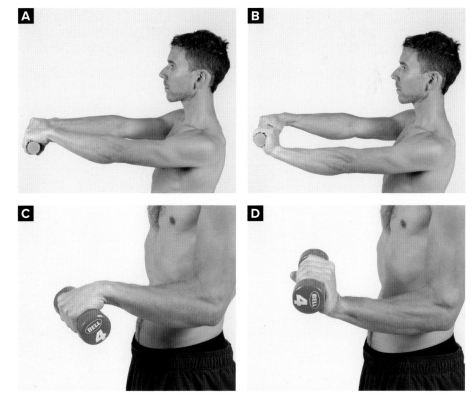

Movement Re-education

Dangerous Movements	Correct Movements
Grip with extended wrist	Keep a neutral wrist
Elbows deviate away from wall	Angle elbow aligned with wrist
Hand jams in a wide crack	Twist your wrist inside wide cracks

Movement Advice

When grasping climbing holds it is common for the wrist to extend back. This position is used because grip strength is stronger when the wrist is extended back 35 degrees. When the wrist extends back 35 degrees, additional muscles that attach to the back of your fingers (finger extensors) aid in stabilizing your grip. The muscles in the back of the wrist attach to the outside of the elbow. Gripping with an extended wrist increases stress on their attachment to outside of the elbow and can cause pain. To avoid excessive wrist extension, keep a neutral wrist while gripping and allow your elbow to angle in closer to the wall. When hand jamming wide cracks there is a tendency to extend your wrist backwards to fill up the space in the crack. Instead of extending your wrist try turning the wrist inside the crack to secure your hand jam.

Grip with an extended wrist

Grip with a neutral wrist

STEPH DAVIS
Rock Climber, Base Jumper, Wingsuit Flyer, Numerous First Ascents and Free Solos

I started campus-board training a few years ago. After a few weeks into my first training cycle I started feeling pain in my elbow. I got nervous about it and I asked a friend what I could do. He told me to sit down, rest my forearm on my thigh and rotate my wrist back and forth for 10-15 slow repetitions with a light dumbbell. My elbow pain stopped immediately and never bothered me again.

Steph Davis on Swedin-Ringle, 5.12-. Indian Creek, Utah. Photo Credit: Tommy Chandler

Rock Rehab Pyramid: Lateral Epicondylosis

Below is the Rock Rehab Pyramid designed to rehabilitate and prevent a lateral epicondylosis injury.

It is made up of four phases: unload, mobility, strength and movement. Begin at the bottom phase of the pyramid. Once you are able to perform all of the prescribed exercises in a given phase of the pyramid without pain then you can progress up the pyramid to the next phase.

Do not perform exercises if they are painful. There is no exact formula for how long it takes a climber to progress back to climbing. Injury recovery times are highly variable and based on individual factors.

If you have any questions regarding the prevention and rehabilitation exercises you should consult your medical professional.

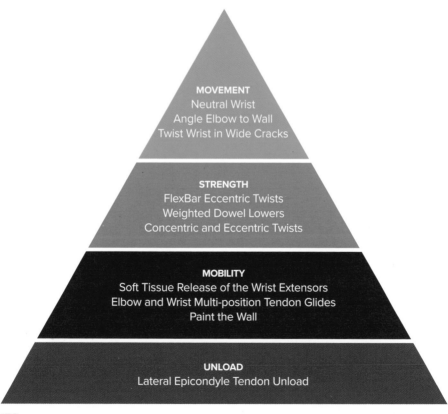

MOVEMENT
Neutral Wrist
Angle Elbow to Wall
Twist Wrist in Wide Cracks

STRENGTH
FlexBar Eccentric Twists
Weighted Dowel Lowers
Concentric and Eccentric Twists

MOBILITY
Soft Tissue Release of the Wrist Extensors
Elbow and Wrist Multi-position Tendon Glides
Paint the Wall

UNLOAD
Lateral Epicondyle Tendon Unload

MEDIAL EPICONDYLOSIS

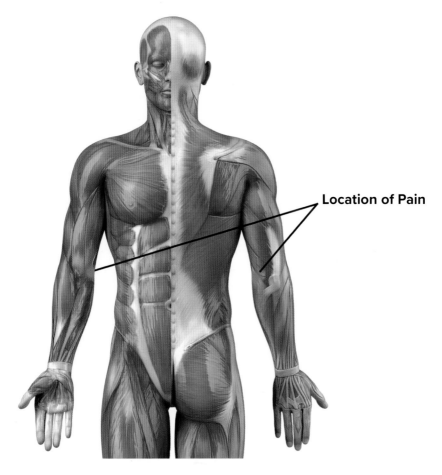

Location of Pain

Signs and Symptoms
- Painful localized point along the inside of the forearm
- Discomfort with actively flexing the wrist forward
- Discomfort with passively extending the wrist backwards

Cause
When you climb, you are constantly overworking the finger and wrist flexors in the front of your forearm by gripping. The repetitive action of constantly flexing your fingers and wrist can lead to degeneration of the shared tendon as it inserts into the bone. You should be aware of dangerous movements that can increase the stress on the finger and wrist flexors tendon and eventually lead to pain and injury. These movements include over-gripping, gripping with a flexed hand and sagging your hips too far away from the wall.

Unloading: Medial Epicondyle Tendon Unload

Instructions
Find your media epicondyle, which is the knobby bone on the inside of your elbow. Cut four strips of rigid strap tape into 8-10 cm pieces. Flex your elbow to 20 degrees.

A, B, C, D Apply cover-role in a diamond shaped pattern around the medial epicondyle of the elbow.

E, F, G, H, I Place the leukotape on top of the cover-role. Secure one end down by pressing firmly. Pull the other end towards the elbow with the desired tension.

What It Does
The tape puts the tendon on slack by taking up the tension in the soft tissue surrounding it. This can lead to decreased pain and increased strength.

Frequency
Tape as needed. The tape is very rigid and may limit range of motion while climbing. It is for this reason that it is recommended to wear during the day to unload the elbow and not during climbing.

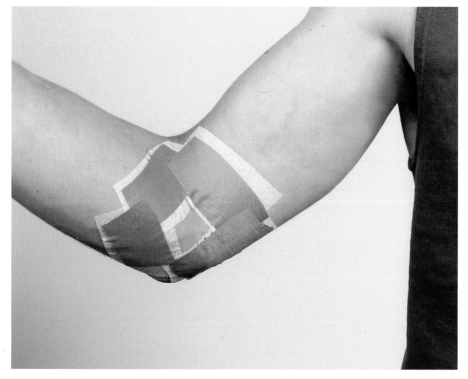

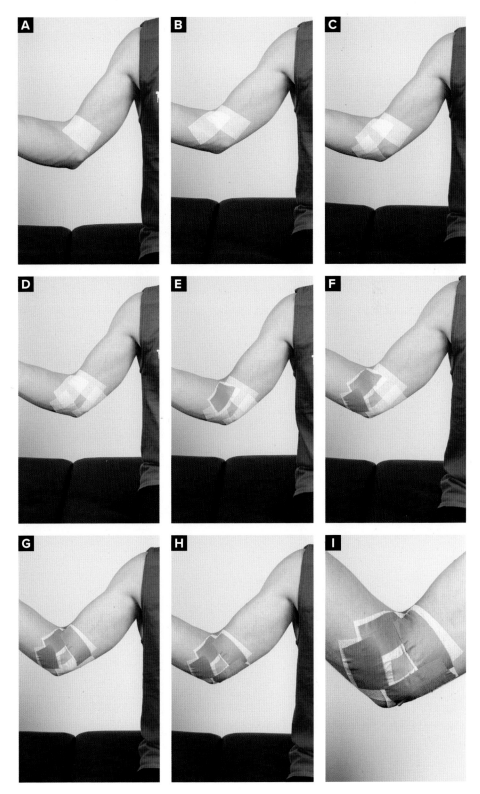

159

Mobility Level 1: Soft Tissue Release of Wrist Flexors

Instructions
A Target your inside forearm muscles by finding the tightest location along the muscle. Flex your wrist and clamp down on the device.

B Keep pressure on the device and straighten your wrist to neutral to create an active release of the soft tissue.

C Perform using a lacrosse ball or soup can.

What It Does
Releases the tension in the wrist extensor muscles in the back of your forearm. Massaging this muscle takes the stress off the tendon.

Frequency
8-10 minutes up to 3 times per day.

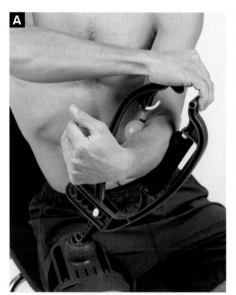
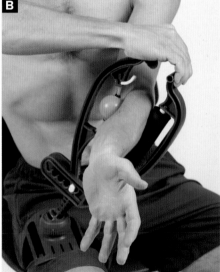

BEN RUECK
5.14 Trad Climber, 5.14 Sport Climber and 5.13 Big Wall Climber

Compressive moves can increase the stress on the inner elbow. Performing compression moves is like wrestling a refrigerator. To avoiding injury during these movements, it is important to balance the pressure between your arms and your legs. Coordinate each arm with the opposite leg to find a balance point where you exert minimal effort. This will improve your climbing efficiency and prevent injury.

Benjamin Rueck on The Free Route, 5.12a. The Totem Pole. Tasmania, Australia. Photo Credit: Andrew Burr

Mobility Level 1 and 2: Elbow and Wrist Multi-Position Tendon Glides and Paint the Wall

A detailed description can be found on pages 146 and 147.

Strength Level 1: Wrist Extension/Rotation

Instructions

A Grasp the handle of a hammer with your elbow at your side and bent to 90 degrees. Keep your palm facing down and slightly flexed.

B Rotate the hammer upward while extending your wrist back until the hammer is perpendicular to the ground.

What It Does

Strengthens your wrist extensors and supinators, which are the antagonists muscles for your wrist flexors and pronators. Your wrist flexors and pronators attach to your medial epicondyle. Strengthening the antagonist muscles helps take stress off the medial epicondyle.

Frequency

3 sets of 15 repetitions once per day.

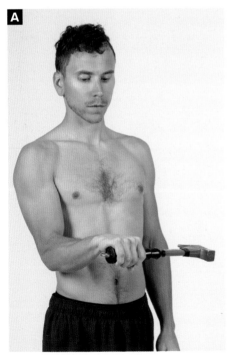
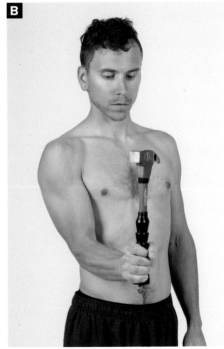

Strength Level 2: Extension/Rotation with Resistance

Instructions

A Wrap a TheraBand around your hand several times. Take the loose end of the band from over the top of your hand and step on it with your opposite foot to secure it to the ground. Make sure the band is passing over the top of the thumb side of your hand and down to your foot. Stand with your elbow at your side and your palm facing down and slightly flexed.

B Extend the wrist back as you rotate your palm upwards. Slowly allow the band to pull you back into the starting position.

What It Does

Strengthens your wrist extensors and supinators to take stress off the medial epicondyle. This is a progression of the wrist extension and rotation with a hammer exercise.

Frequency

3 sets of 15 repetitions once per day.

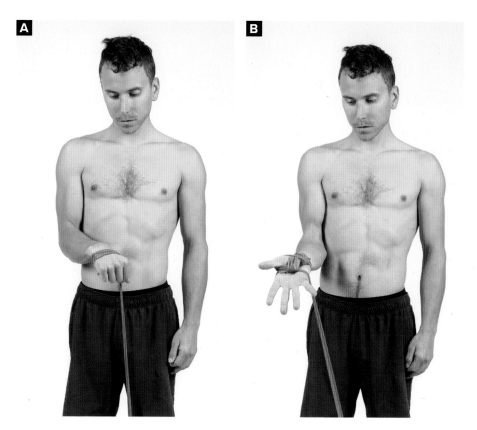

Strength Level 3: Eccentric Extension/Rotation

Instructions

A Grasp the edge of a weight, wine bottle, hammer or frying pan. Stand with your elbow at your side and your palm facing down and slightly flexed.

B Extend your wrist back as you rotate your palm upwards. After you reach the end of the motion, passively assist the weight back to the starting position with your opposite hand to make the exercise purely eccentric.

What It Does

Targets your wrist flexors and pronators eccentrically to strengthen the tendon that attaches to your medial epicondyle.

Frequency

3 sets of 15 repetitions once per day.

> **DIRTBAG TIPS**
> You can perform any of the wrist extension and rotation strength exercises with a wine bottle, hammer, frying pan, ice axe or similar object that is weighted slightly on its end.

Movement Re-education

Dangerous Movements	Correct Movements
Over-gripping holds	Decrease anxiety and soften grip
Gripping with a flexed wrist	Grip with a neutral wrist
Hips sagging from wall	Bring hips closer into the wall

Movement Advice

When climbing challenging routes, it is common to over-grip the holds. This may be a result of fear, anxiety or just poor technique. Over-gripping increases the stress on the forearm muscles that attach to the inner elbow and can lead to pain. To avoid injury, try focusing on your breath and allowing yourself to only grip as much as necessary to maintain a grasp on the hold. You can also try placing more weight into your legs as this will take the stress off the forearm muscles. Additional strategies that decrease forearm tension include bringing your hips closer to the wall so your center of mass is under your feet as well as maintaining your wrist in a neutral position while gripping.

Over-gripping while climbing

Relaxed grip while climbing

Rock Rehab Pyramid: Medial Epicondylosis

Below is the Rock Rehab Pyramid designed to rehabilitate and prevent a medial epicondylosis injury.

It is made up of four phases: unload, mobility, strength and movement. Begin at the bottom phase of the pyramid. Once you are able to perform all of the prescribed exercises in a given phase of the pyramid without pain then you can progress up the pyramid to the next phase.

Do not perform exercises if they are painful. There is no exact formula for how long it takes a climber to progress back to climbing. Injury recovery times are highly variable and based on individual factors.

If you have any questions regarding the prevention and rehabilitation exercises you should consult your medical professional.

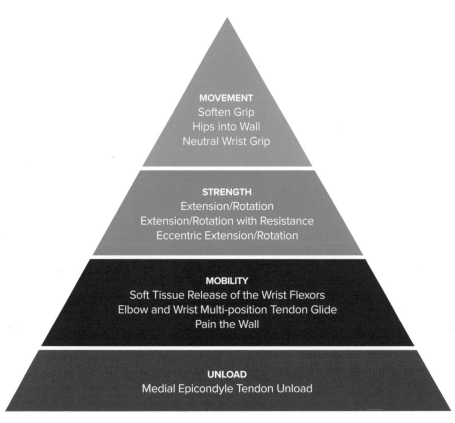

MOVEMENT
Soften Grip
Hips into Wall
Neutral Wrist Grip

STRENGTH
Extension/Rotation
Extension/Rotation with Resistance
Eccentric Extension/Rotation

MOBILITY
Soft Tissue Release of the Wrist Flexors
Elbow and Wrist Multi-position Tendon Glide
Pain the Wall

UNLOAD
Medial Epicondyle Tendon Unload

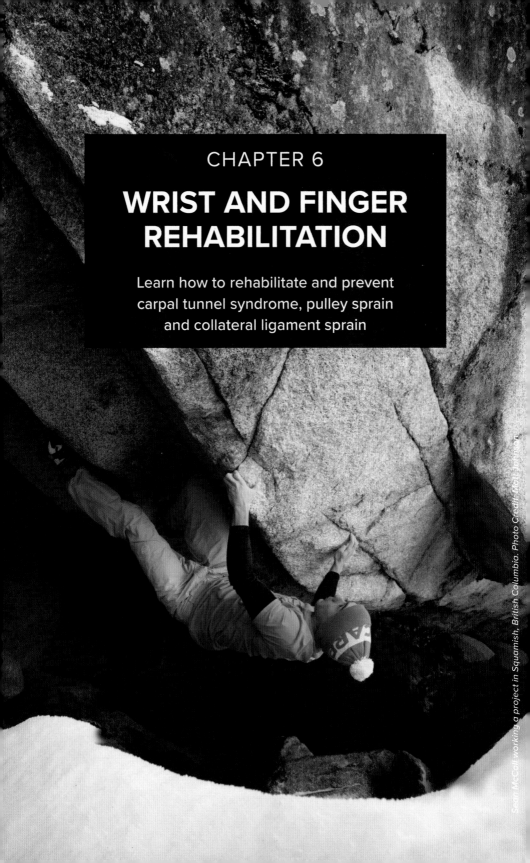

CHAPTER 6

WRIST AND FINGER REHABILITATION

Learn how to rehabilitate and prevent carpal tunnel syndrome, pulley sprain and collateral ligament sprain

CARPAL TUNNEL SYNDROME

 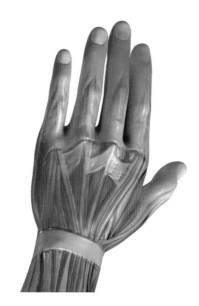

Signs and Symptoms

- Pain in the front of the wrist
- Numbness or tingling into the thumb, index, middle and 1/2 of the ring finger
- Weakness in the hand with a tendency to drop objects
- Increased pain and tingling at night while sleeping

Cause

The median nerve and several tendons from your forearm travel through a small space in your wrist called the carpal tunnel. Often, when the wrist is in a flexed position repetitively, the median nerve can become compressed underneath the tendons in the carpal tunnel. This can cause numbness, pain and weakness in the hand. You should be aware of dangerous movements that can increase the stress on the carpal tunnel and eventually lead to pain and injury. These movements include slopers, underclings and sidepulls. All these movements flex the wrist into extreme positions and can increase the pressure in the carpal tunnel.

Unloading: Carpal Tunnel Circulatory Support

Instructions

A Measure two strips of kinesiology tape from the base of your fingers to the middle of your forearm. Fold the edge of tape 1-2 inches over itself.

B Cut two small triangles in the folded tape. As you unfold the tape the triangles will become diamonds.

C Tear the paper backing off the end of the tape. Slide the diamond holes over the pointer and ring fingers with your palm facing up and the tape facing the inside of your forearm.

D Extend your wrist backwards. Peel the paper off the tape and lay the tape down onto the palm and forearm with no added tension.

E Tear the paper backing off the end of the tape. Slide the diamond holes over the pointer and ring fingers with your palm facing down and the tape facing the outside of your forearm.

F Extend your wrist forwards. Peel the paper off the tape and lay the tape down onto the back of the hand and forearm with no added tension.

G Measure another strip of tape long enough to wrap around the wrist. Remove the backing of the tape at the center. Pull each end of the tape to stretch it to 50%.

H Place the center of the tape over the front of the wrist.

I Wrap the ends of the tape without tension around the wrist.

What It Does

Improves the circulation and stability in the carpal tunnel. It is more effective and less intrusive than splinting. It allows for full range of motion of the wrist while climbing.

Frequency

Tape as needed. Apply 30 minutes prior to climbing. Remove after 48 hours.

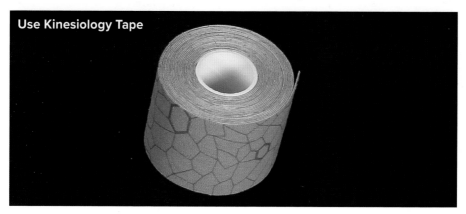

Use Kinesiology Tape

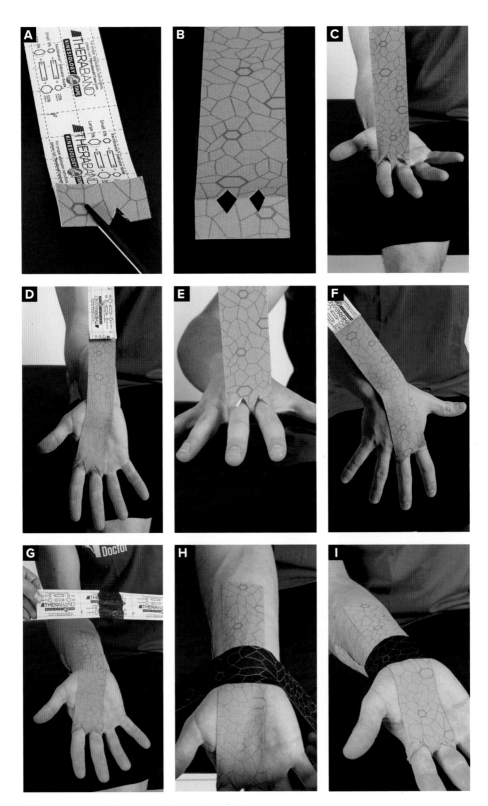

Mobility Level 1: Massage of the Wrist Flexors

DIRTBAG TIPS

You can use your hand, lacrosse ball, soup can or a specialized device such as an Armaid to perform soft tissue release of your muscles.

Instructions

A Target your inside forearm muscles. Place your hand inside the device and apply a firm pressure with your opposite hand.

B Maintain firm pressure on your forearm and move your arm through the device several times from the base of your wrist up to your elbow.

What It Does

Increases the circulation and reduces tension in your forearm muscles and carpal tunnel.

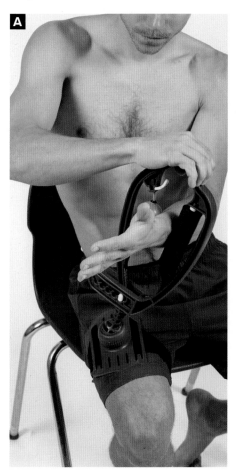
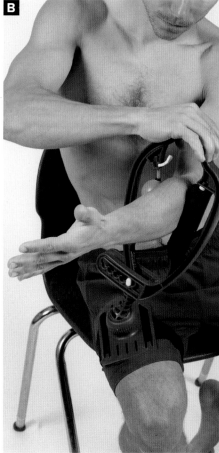

EVA LOPEZ

5.14C Climber, Trainer and Researcher, with a PhD Thesis on Finger Training Methods. Developer of the Transgression Fingerboard.

Before fingerboarding, there are some obvious but often disregarded questions that you must ask yourself:

- Is using a fingerboard advisable given your current condition?
- Have you been climbing routinely and systematically for at least two years so that your tissues have adapted?
- Do you already have a basic technical climbing repertoire?
- Are you more than 16 years of age?

If the answer is yes to all of those questions, the risk for injury due to fingerboarding is similar to other forms of training if you execute, schedule and manage the load properly.

If you are new to fingerboarding, you should opt for the easiest method that has the lowest injury risk but will still produce benefits. This would be low volume, unweighted hangs that avoid failure. If you have more experience fingerboarding and your objective is maximum strength with an emphasis on neural adaptations, varying the edge size and adding weight (when applicable) will help you achieve these goals. It is important to know that leaving several seconds of margin before muscle failure while hanging has a similar effects and less injury risk when compared with training to failure. So when fingerboarding, complete each repetition before failure by finishing a few seconds early.

This does not mean that training to failure is always inadvisable. It has its place from time to time as long as you possess a long training background and have successfully trained with varied margins from 5 to 1 seconds. It will be necessary to train to failure when you want to improve your strength-endurance and maximum strength via hypertrophy (muscle growth). To train for hypertrophy, you can use an intense and moderate-volume method like my "intermittent dead-hangs protocol." You will need to achieve failure in the last repetition either of the last set or of every single set, depending on your training goal and level. You can vary the edge depth and/or add additional weight to achieve this.

Be aware if your technique starts to fail when you flex your elbows, raise your legs or chest, shrug your shoulders, or extend your fingertips. If any of these compensations occur, you will need to lower the load, maintain it just for this occasion, or risk an overuse syndrome in our fingers, elbows and even neck and shoulders.

Eva Lopez trying El Intento, 5.14d (9a), Cuenca, Spain. Photo Credit: Javipec

Mobility Level 2: Finger Tendon Glides

Instructions
Perform the below hand positions in a rhythmic sequence.

A Straight Fingers: Straighten your hand as much as possible.
B Hook Fist: Slowly crimp your fingers down making sure that your knuckles stay aligned with your wrist.
C Full Fist: Roll your fingers downwards.
D Flat Fist: Maximally close this final position.

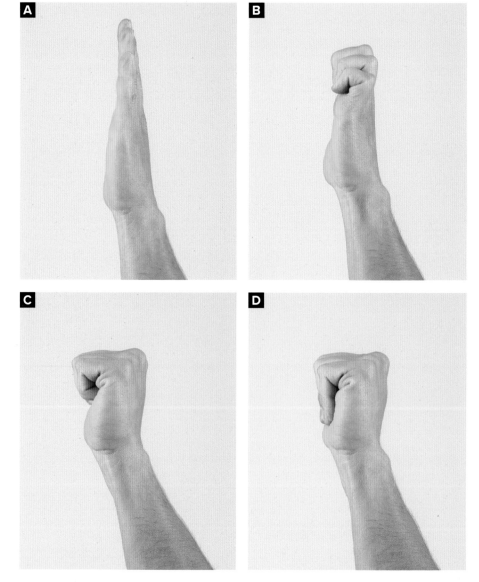

What It Does
By moving the fingers through a full range of motion and keeping the wrist neutral, you glide the tendons underneath the pulley. This promotes tendon healing, reduces pressure and increases mobility, strength and blood flow.

Frequency
3 sets of 10 repetitions up to 3 times per day.

Tips
Progress the tendon glides into more complex movement patterns. You can incorporate tendon glides into climbing-specific movements such as sequencing the moves on your project. These movements should be built into your climbing warm-up routine.

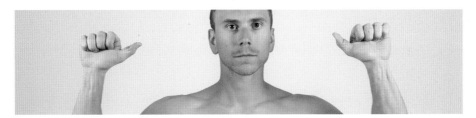

Mobility Level 3: Overhead Drain and Shake

Instructions
A Raise your hand above your head and hold this position for 3-5 seconds.
B Flick your arm downwards so your fingers are facing towards the ground and shake the hand back-and-forth for 3-5 seconds.

What It Does
Carpal tunnel syndrome involves entrapment of the nerves within the wrist. Raising of the hand above the head allows gravity to drain the blood from the wrist. When you rapidly shake the wrist downwards, the blood rushes back into the carpal tunnel. This improves blood flow and circulation.

Frequency
3 sets of 10 repetitions up to 3 times per day.

Tips
Perform the same technique to shake out your hands while climbing. This will help you fight the pump and increase circulation into your carpal tunnel.

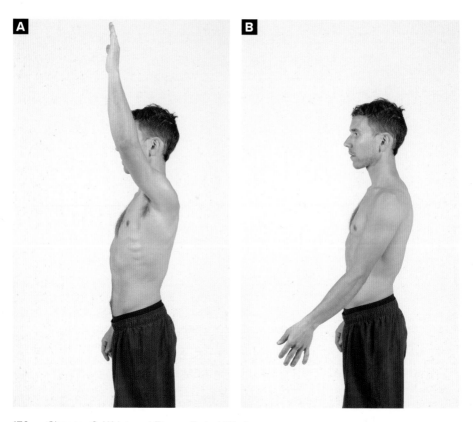

CHRISTIAN CORE

Climbed the World's First Outdoor V16 and Indoor Bouldering World Champion

The campus board is a very useful tool, specifically for symmetrical training, dynamic force, finger strength, motor coordination and control of our bodies. It is meant to integrate and not substitute training for climbing.

Many climbers follow the same exercises seen on Internet videos by people who have been using the campus board for years and at a high level. Instead, it is important to first begin with "simpler" exercises that are less traumatic with fewer repetitions on good ergonomic holds.

The continuous repetitive strain of campus boarding will increase the risk of injury. So when using the board, we must be aware of important details such as: limit cutting loose, avoid full crimping by making an effort to maintain open-hand crimps, not remaining too long with a closed elbow and keeping the wrists as straight as possible. Lastly, the movements must be fluid and controlled.

Translated by Arianna Sanelli

Christian Core on the world's first potential V16, Gioia, Varazze, Italy. Photo Credit: Stella Marchisio

Strength Level 1: Baoding Balls

DIRTBAG TIPS
You can use two smooth rocks instead of the Baoding Balls.

Instructions

A Grasp two smooth rocks or Baoding Balls and rotate them in your hand both counterclockwise and clockwise while keeping a neutral wrist.

B An example of rotating two circular rocks counterclockwise.

C An example of rotating two Baoding Balls clockwise.

What It Does

Glides the tendons within the carpal tunnel and improves circulation without significantly increasing carpal tunnel pressure. Maintaining a neutral wrist while performing this exercise will keep the carpal tunnel pressure in your wrist low.

Frequency

3 sets of 60 seconds up to 3 times per day.

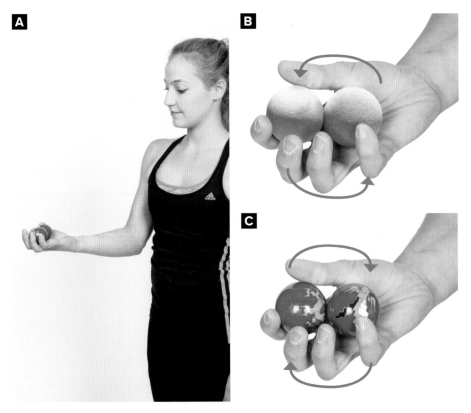

Strength Level 2: Small-Range Band Circles

Instructions

Loop a resistance band around your hand and either hold with your opposite hand or secure in a door. With the elbow bent to 90 degrees at your side perform clockwise and counterclockwise wrist rotations through a small range of motion. Make sure to keep your fingers fully straight while performing the circles.

What It Does

Strengthens the wrist extensor muscles to add more stability to the wrist without significantly increasing carpal tunnel pressure. Large circles should be avoided because they bend the wrist into extreme ranges of motion that increase the pressure in the carpal tunnel. Increased pressure in the carpal tunnel compresses the median nerve and can lead to pain and numbness in the hand. Make sure to use only small circles when performing this exercise.

Frequency

3 sets of 60 seconds once per day.

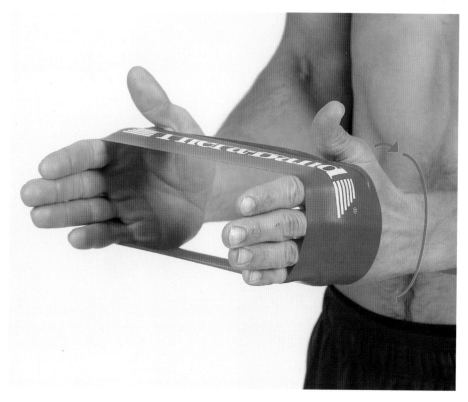

Strength Level 3: Small-Range Rice Bucket Circles

DIRTBAG TIPS
You will need a rice bucket to perform this exercise. If you don't have a rice bucket, you can try the exercise between two couch cushions. If you are on a budget, just add beans to the bucket and cook the rice and beans for dinner after using.

Instructions

A Place the rice bucket on a bench so that it rests at hip level. Place your hand in the rice bucket with a closed fist. Engage your shoulder blade muscles to prevent any movement from your arm and perform miniature rotations of your wrist in the bucket both clockwise and counterclockwise.

B Example of the hand position outside the rice bucket.

What It Does

Stabilizes the wrist without significantly increasing carpal tunnel pressure.

Frequency

3 sets of 60 seconds once per day.

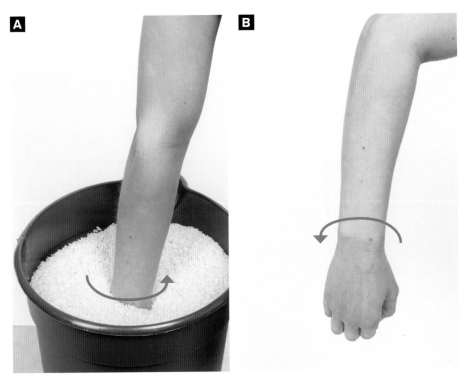

Double Rice Bucket Benefits

It is more natural and ergonomic to use two rice buckets instead of one. When you use two rice buckets your shoulders are placed in a more aligned position.

Don't Forget About Your Shoulder Blades

When performing rice bucket exercises for your fingers and wrist, don't forget that your hands are connected to your body through your shoulder blades. Be attentive to your shoulder blade position and avoid rounding your shoulders forward. Engage the muscles in your shoulder blades to help support your wrists and fingers during rice bucket exercises.

Movement Re-education

Dangerous Movements	Correct Movements
Slopers	Limit the use of slopers
Underclings	Limit the use of underclings
Sidepulls	Limit the use of sidepulls

Change Your Movement

Slopers, underclings and sidepulls all flex the wrist into extreme positions and can increase the pressure in the carpal tunnel. The position of your wrist must be neutral to minimize stress over the carpal tunnel. To reduce the likelihood of injury to the carpal tunnel, it is best to limit the use of these holds. If using such holds is necessary, you should consider minimizing the bend of your wrist while grabbing these holds and placing as much weight as possible onto your feet to decrease the pressure going into the wrist. A great tip for reducing carpal tunnel pressure during a sidepull is to use the outside edge of your opposite foot to accept most of the weight and rotate that hip into the wall to increase stability.

Sloper

Undercling

SASHA DIGIULIAN
First North American Woman to Climb 5.14D, Indoor Climbing Overall World Champion

Flexing your wrist forwards too much on slopers and underclings or extending your wrist backwards too much while crimping can lead to injury from overuse. So it is best to keep your wrist in a neutral position as often as possible while climbing. Also, don't forget that your wrist, via your arm, is attached to your main body or core through your shoulder blade. By keeping your shoulder blades engaged you can actually take stress off your wrist.

Sasha Digiulian on Dures Limites 5.14b (8c). Ceuse, France. Photo Credit: Jensen Walker

Rock Rehab Pyramid: Carpal Tunnel Syndrome

Below is the Rock Rehab Pyramid designed to rehabilitate and prevent a carpal tunnel syndrome injury.

It is made up of four phases: unload, mobility, strength and movement. Begin at the bottom phase of the pyramid. Once you are able to perform all of the prescribed exercises in a given phase of the pyramid without pain then you can progress up the pyramid to the next phase.

Do not perform exercises if they are painful. There is no exact formula for how long it takes a climber to progress back to climbing. Injury recovery times are highly variable and based on individual factors.

If you have any questions regarding the prevention and rehabilitation exercises you should consult your medical professional.

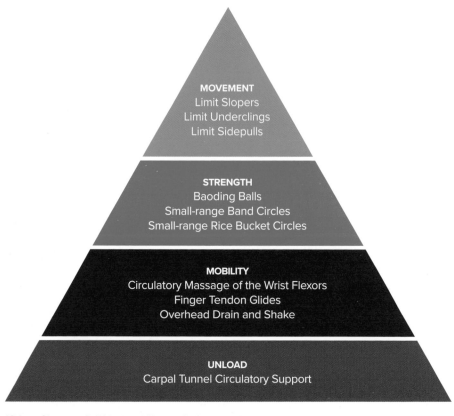

MOVEMENT
Limit Slopers
Limit Underclings
Limit Sidepulls

STRENGTH
Baoding Balls
Small-range Band Circles
Small-range Rice Bucket Circles

MOBILITY
Circulatory Massage of the Wrist Flexors
Finger Tendon Glides
Overhead Drain and Shake

UNLOAD
Carpal Tunnel Circulatory Support

PULLEY SPRAIN

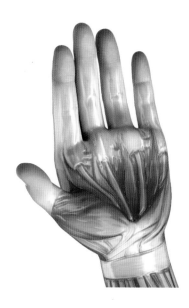

Signs and Symptoms

- Can occur over any digit, but most commonly occurs over the ring finger along the A2 pulley
- Tender to the touch along the injured pulley
- Swelling, redness and inflammation
- Stiffness bending the fingers
- Painful to actively crimp and grip

Cause

The muscles in our forearms extend into long narrow tendons as they reach into the fingers. These tendons run through sheaths and are anchored down by pulleys that keep the tendons gliding flush to the bones. There are five annular pulleys that sling around the bone and four cruciform pulleys that form a cross over the bone to secure the tendon. When excessive strain is placed on the finger tendons, the pressure exerts an outward force on the pulley which may strain or tear it. You should be aware of dangerous movements that can increase the stress on the pulley and eventually lead to pain and injury. These movements include dynamic moves to and from small edges, pulling too much with your fingers on small holds and the repetitive use of full or closed crimps.

Unloading: Circular, Figure 8 and H Taping

It is a climber's personal choice whether or not they choose to tape your fingers when they return to climbing after a pulley injury. If you choose to tape the finger, there are three popular methods. There has been considerable debate about which taping technique is the most effective to reduce tension on the pulleys. Consequently, there is abundant research supporting and refuting the use of different taping methods. Volker Schöffl et al. published a study in 2007 comparing Circular, Figure 8 and H taping. The H taping technique was shown to be more supportive to the pulley than the Figure 8 or Circular taping technique. The study showed that H taping reduces tendon-bone distance by 16% and increases strength in the crimp grip position by 13% compared to the control group without tape. It is based on this study that the H technique is offered as the best taping option when returning to climbing after a pulley injury. It would then be advisable to slowly transition from the H technique to the less supportive taping techniques as the pulley ligament heals.

Unloading: Circular Taping for Structural Support

Instructions
A, B   Wrap the rigid strap tape around the injured pulley 2-3 times using moderate tension. Keep the finger straight when applying the tape.

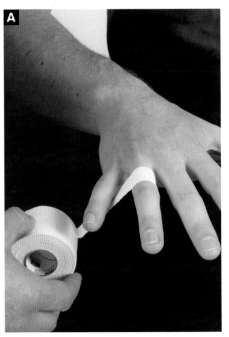
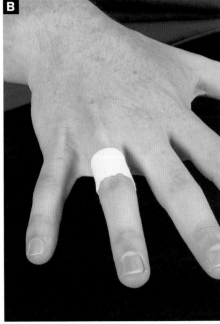

Unloading: Figure 8 Taping for Structural Support

Instructions

A   Wrap the rigid strap tape twice around the base of your finger.

B   Bend the finger to 30 degrees and wrap the tape across the inside of the bent joint.

C, D, E   Wrap twice around the finger above the joint.

F, G, H   Wrap the tape back below the joint forming a cross.
Complete the wrap over the base of the finger.

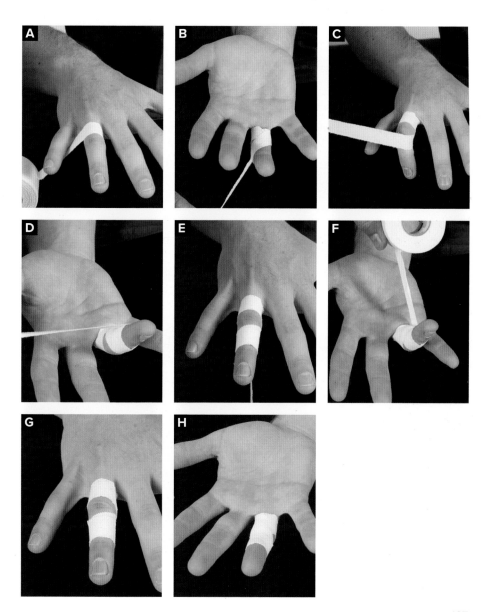

Unloading: H Taping for Structural Support

Instructions

A Cut a rectangle of rigid strap tape 10 cm thick and 2 cm wide. Cut the tape down the center to form the letter H. Make sure to leave approximately 1 cm of tape adjoined at the center.

B Place the bottom of the tape over the base of your finger. The center of the tape should align with the center of your finger joint.

C Wrap the bottom of the tape around the base of your finger.

D Flex the finger 30 degrees and wrap the top of the tape around your finger above the bent joint. Make sure the tape is firm but not too tight. Squeeze the tip of your finger to see if you have adjusted the tension correctly. If it takes longer than 2 seconds for color to return to your finger, then you have taped too tight.

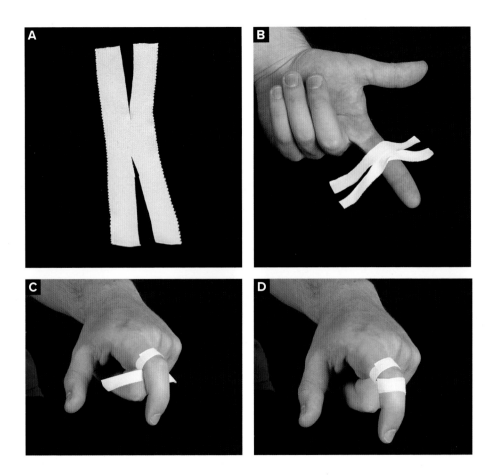

SONNIE TROTTER
5.14 Trad Climber and 5.14D Sport Climber

My story stems from an injury. I was on a sport climbing binge as a teenager and I wanted to see how hard I could climb. So I started putting a lot of energy into training and finger boarding. I was challenging my potential in terms of difficulty but I started to loose the sense of adventure. I got bored with the monotony of chasing grades and training. Then, I injured a finger pretty badly on a difficult route. After my finger injury, I was searching for a deeper reason for what drove me to climb. I realized that what I fell in love with climbing as a teenager was the fun discovery aspect. Where you get to travel to cool places, go to crags with great people and camp under the stars. I wanted adventure, so I went to Yosemite to traditional climb. After climbing in Yosemite, I fell in love with climbing all over again on another level. It is likely I would have never found this passion if it weren't for my injury.

Sonnie Trotter climbing Estado Critico 5.14d (9a). Siurana, Spain. Photo Credit: Cameron Maier

Pulley Taping for Circulatory Support

The goal of applying tape is to unload the pulley ligament to allow a gradual return to climbing. Taping should not be used for more than eight weeks because it can lead to the pulley becoming weaker and relying on the support from the tape.

This is why taping should be done in a sequenced regression. Meaning that you should start taping with strong tape and slowly regress towards a weaker tape. This sequence allows you to continue to climb but to decrease the reliance on using tape to support the pulleys.

Start with the most rigid tape, which would be leukotape. After three weeks, switch to a moderately rigid tape such as white athletic tape. After three more weeks, use a non-structurally supportive tape such as kinesiology tape.

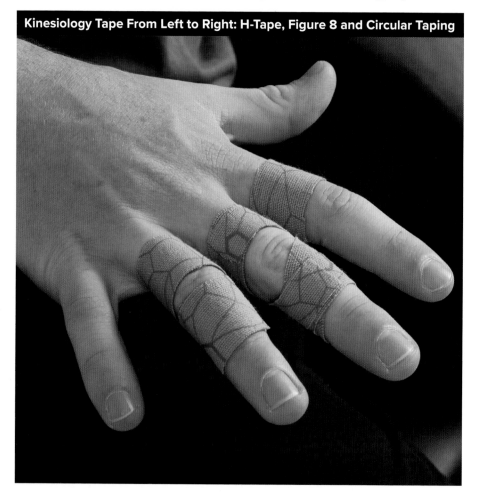

Kinesiology Tape From Left to Right: H-Tape, Figure 8 and Circular Taping

Mobility Level 1: Circulatory Massage of the Finger

Instructions

A Slide an acupressure ring back and forth on your finger while pressing gently into the ring.

B Make a fist with your opposite hand. Apply lotion to your finger. Slide your injured finger in and out of your fist. It may be wise to perform this technique in the privacy of your own home. In the United States this motion is seen as an obscene and sexually evocative gesture.

What It Does

Increases the circulation to the fingers. The fingers are far from the heart and pulleys lack adequate blood flow. It is important to increase the amount of blood to the pulley to improve healing time.

Frequency

6-8 minutes up to 3 times per day.

> **DIRTBAG TIPS**
> If you don't have an acupressure ring, use lotion and your palm instead.

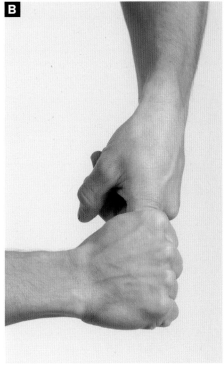

Mobility Level 2: Finger Tendon Glides

A detailed description with photographs can be found on page 174.

Mobility Level 3: Lumbrical, Claw and Extension Stretch

Instructions Performed on the Right Index Finger

A Lumbrical Stretching: Bend the middle joint in your finger and extend the base of your finger backwards by pressing on the top of the middle joint.

B Claw Stretching: Place your hand in a hook position and add overpressure with the opposite hand.

C Extension Stretching: Extend the finger backwards until a stretch is felt. Do not hyperextend the middle or final joints of the finger.

What It Does
Increases the mobility of the muscles, tendons and joints in the finger.

Frequency
3 sets of 30-second holds up to 3 times per day.

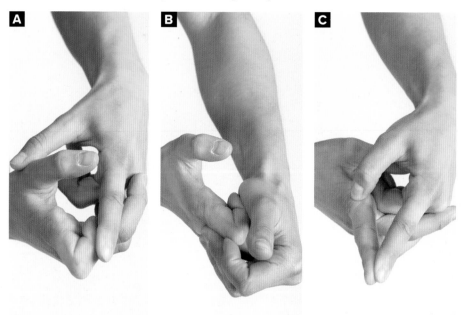

JONATHAN SIEGRIST

Multiple 5.15A Ascents and 5.14 Flashes, 196 5.14 Ascents, Several Big Walls up to 5.13+

I've never ruptured a tendon but at times I have had sore fingers from pulling on pockets and monos. To prevent serious finger injuries from occurring, I have found it helpful to perform strength exercises for the muscles and tendons in the back of the fingers. Pressing the fingers outwards in a rice bucket or against the resistance of a rubber-band are two great methods to keep these muscles strong. You can find the perfect sized rubber-band at the supermarket. They are usually wrapped around pieces of asparagus or broccoli. I typically just wear the band around my wrist. Wearing it around my wrist serves as a reminder for me to perform the exercises during my down time when I am resting or watching television.

Jonathan Siegrist on the first ascent of I am the Walrus 5.14b. Boulder, CO. Photo Credit: Cameron Maier

Strength Level 1: Resisted Finger Expansions

Instructions

A   Place a rubber-band around the tips of your fingers while maintaining a straight wrist.

B, C   Spread your fingers apart without bending your wrist.

What It Does

This exercise strengthens the muscles in the fingers that help support and equalize the pressure on the pulleys. Perform isometric holds at varied angles to mirror the muscle actions of the fingers while climbing.

Frequency

3 sets of 15 repetitions with a 5-second isometric hold once per day.

> **DIRTBAG TIPS**
> Use several rubber bands around your fingers to increase the resistance. You can find thick rubber bands in the vegetable section of the grocery market. They are usually wrapped around asparagus and broccoli.

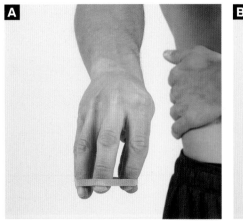

Strength Level 1: Variation

Instructions

A Place your fingers inside a resisted device such as a Metolius GripSaver.

B Spread your fingers while keeping your wrist straight.

C You can use a TheraBand Hand X-Trainer.

D You can use PowerFingers.

What It Does

Strengthens the finger extensor muscles in the back of the hand and fingers. These muscles help protect the structures in the front of the hand such as the tendons and pulleys. This is a variation of the resisted finger expansions with the rubber-band.

Frequency

3 sets of 15 repetitions with a 5-second isometric hold once per day.

Tips

To make this exercise more functional you can squat into a climbing position and raise your arm into the air while performing the exercise.

A
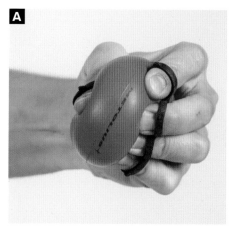

B
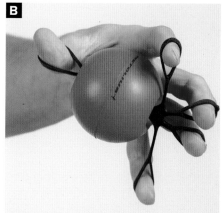

C

D
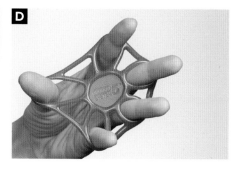

ADAM ONDRA

5.15C Climber and First Ascents, 3-Time World Champion in Lead, Boulder and Overall

Many climbers are advised not to crimp, because the tension on the fingers is higher. But all the very minor injuries I have had, such as a little pain for a few days, have been from open-hand crimps or two-finger pockets.

The pain was always due to a type of hold where most of the load was on one finger; my ring finger. I would position my hand in the hold this way because the hold was sharper (i.e. better to hold) at that part. These kinds of holds are in my opinion the most dangerous ones. I feel that in some cases crimping is a safer option on these holds because it equalizes the load across more of the fingers.

When it comes to preventing finger injuries, it is the best to adopt a universal approach in the way you grab holds. Don't be too monolithic. If you only crimp or if you only open hand, tendons are always strained in the same way. Utilizing a variety of grips can not only help to prevent injuries but also improve your climbing efficiency.

A varied approach is also important when choosing climbing destinations. Visiting various crags and climbing on different rocks helps diversify your technique. It limits overuse injury, is more fun and makes you a better overall climber.

Adam Ondra on Vicious Circle, 5.15a/b (9a+/b). Tadej's cave, Slovenia. Photo Credit: Javipec

Strength Level 2: Rice Bucket Finger Expansions

Instructions

A Place your hand in a rice bucket making sure to keep your wrist neutral and fingers slightly flexed.

B Open your hand by spreading and straightening your fingers and thumb against the resistance of the rice.

C This photo shows an example of the start of the exercise with the hand in a rice bucket.

What It Does

Strengthens the finger extensor muscles in the back of the hand that help protect the structures such as pulley ligaments in the front of the hand.

Frequency

3 sets of 60 seconds once per day.

Tips

The motion occurs in two parts. The first is the spreading of the fingers wide and the second is the straightening of the fingers backwards.

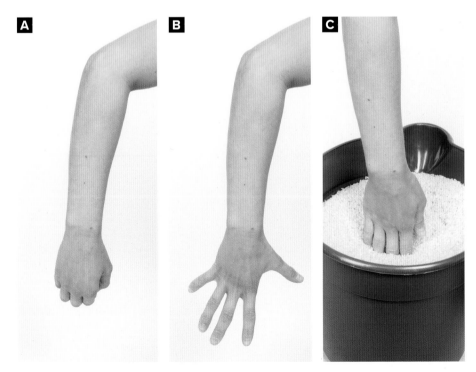

Strength Level 3: Weighted Fingertip Hangs

Instructions

A Girth hitch a light weight, approximately 2-3 pounds, to a piece of shoulder-length webbing. Loop the other end around the tip of your finger. Hold the weight statically off the ground.

B If you do not have a weight to hang from the webbing you can use your foot to apply pressure.

What It Does

Begins to load the finger flexors and the pulleys in a safe, controlled and measurable way.

Frequency

3 sets of 60-second hangs once per day.

Tips

Wait until at least 6 weeks after a pulley injury to perform. You can slowly increase the weight that you hang every 2 weeks. Do not perform this exercise if there is pain. You can progress this exercise to gentle assisted hangboarding.

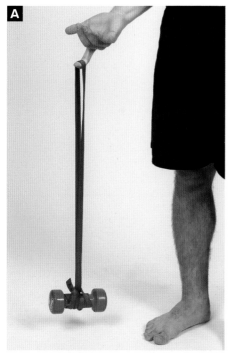
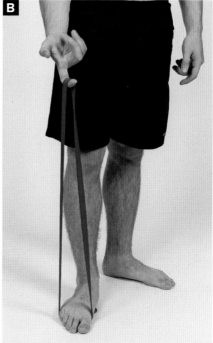

Movement Re-education

Dangerous Movements	Correct Movements
Pulling to move from small holds	Push with your feet
Dynamic moves on small edges	Perform more static movements
Full and closed crimp grips	Use half crimp or open hand grips

Movement Advice

Dynamic moves to and from small edges, pulling too much with your fingers on small holds and the repetitive use of full or closed crimps, can all increase the stress on the pulley. Try to perform large moves from small edges more statically and push with your feet instead of pulling with your fingers. To avoid injury, use an open-hand grip over a crimp. However, this is not a rule. The nature of the hold will determine the safest grip. If a crimp is needed, then utilize first a half crimp, then a closed crimp and finally as a last resort a full crimp. A half crimp is the preferred crimp because it spreads the load more evenly between the tendons and pulleys. Closed crimps are preferred over full crimps. The force generated with the closed crimp is 17% more than the full crimp. The closed-crimp grip does so without increasing strain to the middle and ring fingers, which are the most susceptible to pulley injuries, although it does increase strain on the index finger.

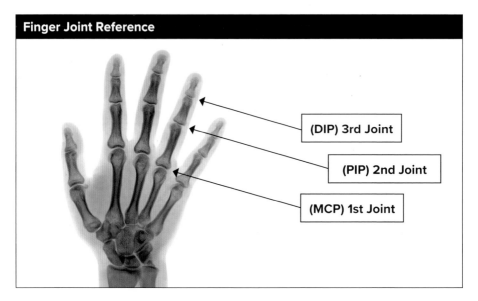

Finger Joint Reference

(DIP) 3rd Joint

(PIP) 2nd Joint

(MCP) 1st Joint

Pro Advice

SEAN MCCOLL

3-time Adult World Champion and 5-time Junior World Champion

I was taught at an early age to use an open-hand grip. I use that now
on 90% of the holds. If I need to crimp hard, I will use a half crimp.
Physiologically a half crimp is a weaker grip than a full crimp. However,
since I trained my half crimp at such a young age it developed into my
strongest grip. The benefits of a full and closed crimp are that you can
rotate the wrist more freely and lock off past your shoulder. This can give
you and extra 2-3 inches. So I still use this grip but only on certain moves.

Sean McColl chalking up at the World Cup Finals. Briancon, France. Photo Credit: Eddie Fowke

Gripping-Position Reference

Below are four of the more common grip positions. Typically, the thumb rests next to index finger for the half and full crimp, but is depicted away from the index finger in the photo in order to visualize the angle of the third joint (DIP) more clearly.

Open-Hand Grip
Minimal bend of the first, second and third joints in the fingers.

Half Crimp
Bend of the first and second joint and no hyperextension of the third joint.

Full Crimp
Bend of the first and second joint and hyperextension of the third joint.

Closed Crimp
Bend of the first and second joint. Hyperextension of the third joint. The pad of the thumb is pressed on top of the tip of the pointer finger.

Open-Hand Grip

Half Crimp

Full Crimp

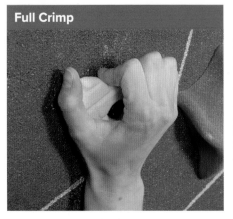

Closed Crimp

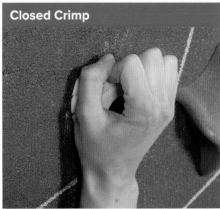

Rock Rehab Pyramid: Pulley Sprain

Below is the Rock Rehab Pyramid designed to rehabilitate and prevent a pulley sprain injury.

It is made up of four phases: unload, mobility, strength and movement. Begin at the bottom phase of the pyramid. Once you are able to perform all of the prescribed exercises in a given phase of the pyramid without pain then you can progress up the pyramid to the next phase.

Do not perform exercises if they are painful. There is no exact formula for how long it takes a climber to progress back to climbing. Injury recovery times are highly variable and based on individual factors.

If you have any questions regarding the prevention and rehabilitation exercises you should consult your medical professional.

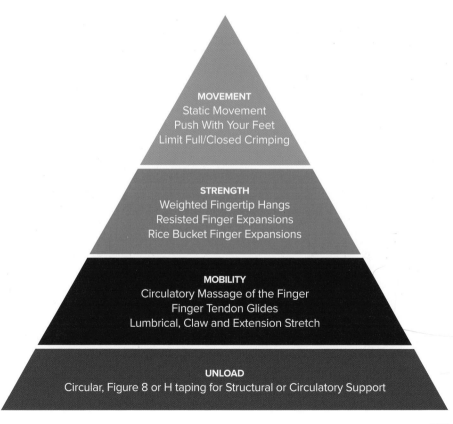

MOVEMENT
Static Movement
Push With Your Feet
Limit Full/Closed Crimping

STRENGTH
Weighted Fingertip Hangs
Resisted Finger Expansions
Rice Bucket Finger Expansions

MOBILITY
Circulatory Massage of the Finger
Finger Tendon Glides
Lumbrical, Claw and Extension Stretch

UNLOAD
Circular, Figure 8 or H taping for Structural or Circulatory Support

COLLATERAL LIGAMENT SPRAIN

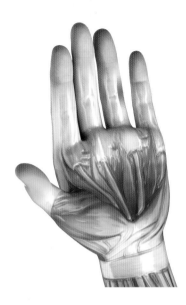
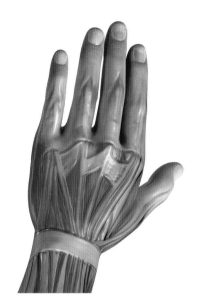

Signs and Symptoms
- Pain on the side of the finger over the injured ligament
- Excessive sideways motion of the injured finger away from the painful side of the finger
- Swelling, redness and inflammation
- Painful to bend the finger side to side

Cause

The finger joints are supported laterally on each side by collateral ligaments. They stabilize the finger from side-to-side movement. When you climb, your hand and fingers are placed in aggressive positions that may put increased force into the ligament, causing it to tear. You should be aware of dangerous movements that can increase the stress on the collateral ligaments and eventually lead to pain and injury. These movements include finger locks in thin cracks, slanted far-to-reach holds and dynamic movements upwards from a gaston or sidepull.

Unloading: Sidesplint Taping for Structural Support

Instructions

A Wrap rigid strap tape below the lower knuckle of your injured finger.

B Wrap a second strip of rigid strap tape above the lower knuckle of your injured finger.

C Cut three thin strips of tape that measure slightly less than the distance between the anchors.

D Align the strips of tape on top of each other so that they taper in the middle and fan out at the ends.

E Attach the end of the fanned strip of tape to the tape below your knuckle on the same side as your painful collateral ligament.

F Secure the fanned strip by wrapping a piece of tape below the knuckle. You can choose to bend your finger 20-30 degrees before attaching if you would like to increase the support of the tape.

G Bend your finger to the painful side with your opposite hand and firmly attach the other end of the fanned strip to the anchor above the knuckle.

H Secure the fanned strip by wrapping a piece of tape above the knuckle.

I Complete the taping technique

What It Does
Creates a structural support to the collateral ligament in the finger.

Frequency
Tape as needed. Apply 30 minutes prior to climbing.

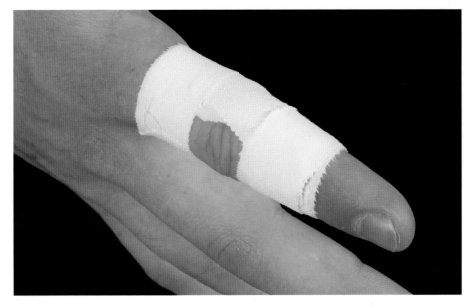

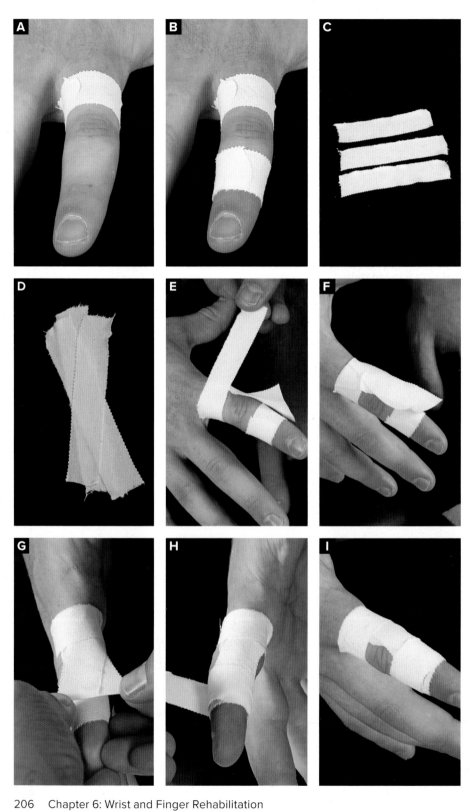

PAUL ROBINSON
World-Class Boulderer with Multiple V15 Ascents

I started climbing when I was 11 years old. I was 14 when I had my first injury. It was a fractured growth plate in my finger from climbing too much. I had to take six weeks off from climbing. I never had a coach, so when I was younger, I wasn't aware if I was climbing too much. I wish I could have been more mature about my injury and more aware of the warning signs. When you are young, even if you feel injured, you don't let yourself believe it. It's hard to see the big picture. You just want to keep pushing and climbing harder. However, you can't get stronger when you're injured. So it is best to take a step back and listen to your body. You need to be okay with a small step back in order to push yourself forward. Take a week off when your fingers are sore instead of having to take six weeks off after they are further damaged. Preventing an injury is far better than dealing with the consequences.

Paul Robinson on Kung Fury Sit, Red Rocks Nevada. Photo Credit: Alexandra Kahn

Unloading: Buddy Taping for Structural Support

Instructions

Apply a strip of rigid strap tape both above and below the injured joint. Buddy tape should adjoin the injured finger with the finger that is adjacent to the painful side. For example, if the inside of the ring finger has pain, then tape the inside of the ring finger next to the middle finger.

What It Does

Buddy taping uses an additional finger to brace or support the lateral motion of your injured finger that stresses the collateral ligament.

Frequency

Tape as needed. Apply 30 minutes prior to climbing.

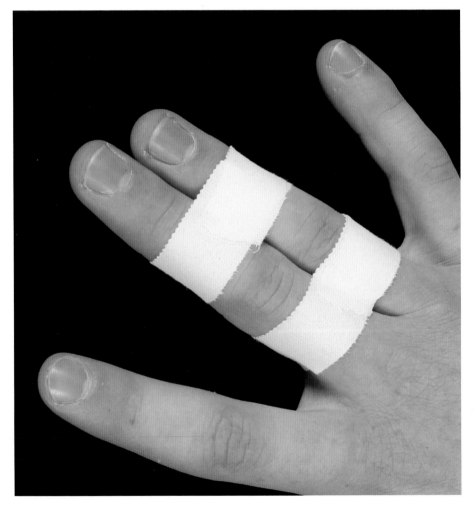

Mobility Level 1, 2 and 3: Circulatory Massage of the Finger, Finger Tendon Glides, Lumbrical, Claw and Extension Stretch

A detailed description can be found on pages 191, 174 and 192.

Strength Level 1: Lateral Isometrics

Instructions for a Middle Finger Collateral Ligament Sprain

A Rest your injured finger next to the finger to its right. Press your opposite fingertips on the joint and resist outwards.

B Rest your injured finger next to the finger to its left. Press your opposite fingertips on the joint and resist outwards.

What It Does
Stabilizes the muscles, joints and ligaments on the sides of the finger.

Frequency
3 sets of 15 repetitions with a 5-second isometric hold once per day.

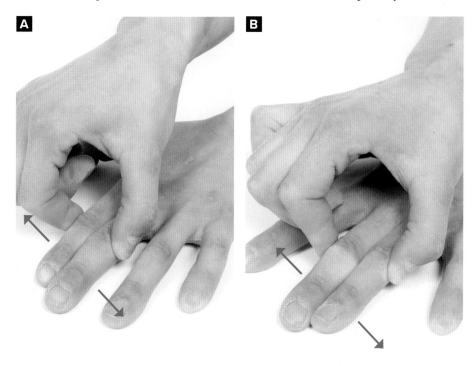

Strength Level 2: Resisted Lateral Slides

Instructions for a Ring Finger Collateral Ligament Sprain
A Place a rubber-band around the outside of the joint of the injured finger.
B Press your finger against the resistance of the rubber-band.
C Place a rubber-band around the inside of your injured finger.
D Press your finger against the resistance of the rubber-band.

What It Does
Stabilizes the muscles, joints and ligaments on the sides of the finger.

Frequency
3 sets of 15 repetitions with a 5-second isometric hold once per day.

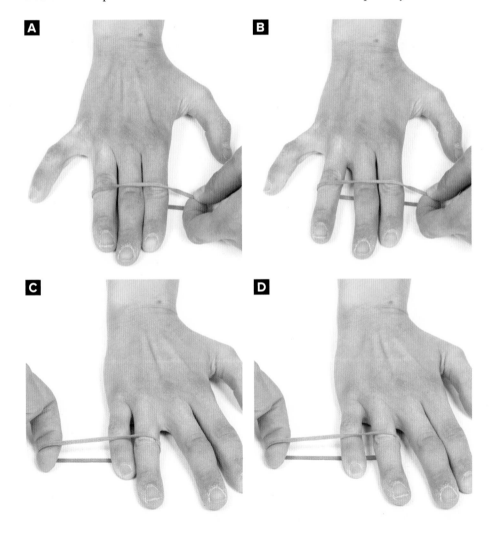

Strength Level 3: Rice Bucket Splays

Instructions
A, C   Place your hand in a rice bucket with your fingers pressed together.
B, D   Splay your fingers apart by pressing outwards into the rice. Bring your fingers back to the starting position.

What It Does
Stabilizes the muscles, joints and ligaments on the sides of the finger.

Frequency
3 sets of 60 seconds once per day.

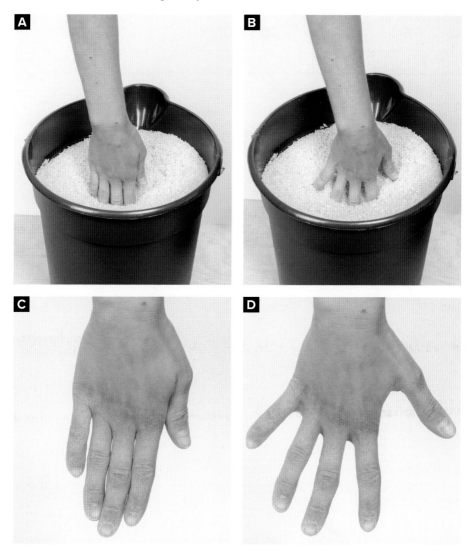

Movement Re-education

Dangerous Movements	Correct Movements
Finger-locks	Weight your feet
Slanted holds	Position elbow in line with wrist
Dynamic moves from a sidebent wrist	Perform static moves

Movement Advice

Finger locks in thin cracks, slanted far-to-reach holds and dynamic movement upward from a gaston or sidepull can all increase the stress on the collateral ligaments in the finger. To avoid injury, put the majority of weight into your feet when finger locking. Push your body upwards with your legs instead of pulling hard with your fingers. When reaching for far slanted holds try to position your wrist and elbow in line with the hold, rather than having your wrist cocked to the side. Perform static movements as often as possible when moving upward from a gaston or sidepull move.

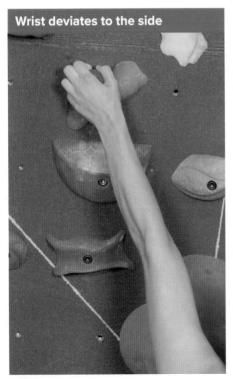
Wrist deviates to the side

Neutral wrist position

Pro Advice

HANS FLORINE
Holds the Speed Record on the Nose and Indoor Speed Climbing World Champion

I always contrast-bath my hands between an ice-bucket and a warm-water bucket after climbing hard. It is easy to do. Shove your hands in an ice bucket until you can't bear it anymore, which may be 30 seconds to 2 minutes. Take your hands out and put them into a bucket of warm water until they thaw. Then put your hands back into the ice bucket. Three times in each bucket is enough to make the hands nimble. Any climber knows that when they stress their hands really hard, they'll fall asleep and wake-up with their hands in a claw position. If you contrast-bath, they won't be that way when you wake up. It's a great way to flush your hands and increase the circulation.

Hans Florine on the Nose of El Capitan. Yosemite, California. Photo Credit: Jim Thornburg

Rock Rehab Pyramid: Collateral Ligament Sprain

Below is the Rock Rehab Pyramid designed to rehabilitate and prevent a collateral ligament sprain injury.

It is made up of four phases: unload, mobility, strength and movement. Begin at the bottom phase of the pyramid. Once you are able to perform all of the prescribed exercises in a given phase of the pyramid without pain then you can progress up the pyramid to the next phase.

Do not perform exercises if they are painful. There is no exact formula for how long it takes a climber to progress back to climbing. Injury recovery times are highly variable and based on individual factors.

If you have any questions regarding the prevention and rehabilitation exercises you should consult your medical professional.

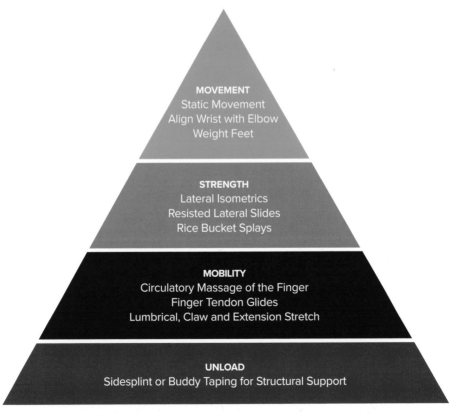

MOVEMENT
Static Movement
Align Wrist with Elbow
Weight Feet

STRENGTH
Lateral Isometrics
Resisted Lateral Slides
Rice Bucket Splays

MOBILITY
Circulatory Massage of the Finger
Finger Tendon Glides
Lumbrical, Claw and Extension Stretch

UNLOAD
Sidesplint or Buddy Taping for Structural Support

CHAPTER 7

NERVE MOBILITY

Learn the concept of neurodynamics and how to use mobilization exercises to treat nerve pain.

Numbness, Tingling and Radiating Pain

Nerves in the Body	Front Ulnar / Back Ulnar
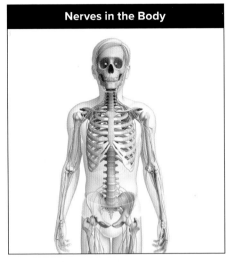	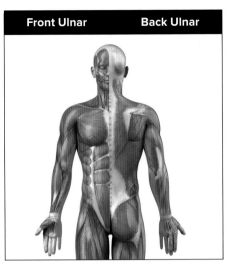

Front Radial / Back Radial	Front Median / Back Median
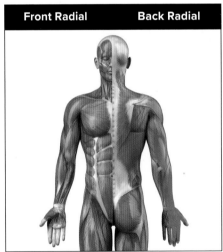	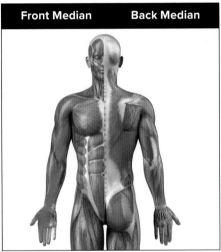

Signs and Symptoms
- Pain that radiates into the arm and/or fingers
- Numbness and/or tingling
- Weakness in the hand with a tendency to drop objects
- Increased symptoms at night while sleeping

Cause
Nerves in the upper body exit through the neck and travel past the shoulder, elbow and wrist into the fingers. Nerves often become entrapped underneath tight muscles and lead to pain or numbness in the arm, hand and fingers.

Nerve Mobility

Imagine that you are belaying your climbing partner and they are stuck at the crux. They keep climbing up and down-climbing but they aren't going anywhere. You look at your belay device and you see the rope glide back and forth, gaining either more tension or slack.

This is how nerves move throughout in your body. They connect from the brain and spinal cord to your muscles. As you move, nerves tension and slacken several millimeters between the layers of muscle. Below is an example of how nerves tension and slacken just like a climbing rope. The curved lines represent slackened nerves while the straight lines represent tensioned nerves.

A Tensions the median nerve across the elbow, wrist and fingers.
B Slackens the median nerve across the elbow, wrist and fingers.
C Tensions the ulnar nerve across the neck, elbow, wrist and fingers.
D Slackens the ulnar nerve across the neck, elbow, wrist and fingers.

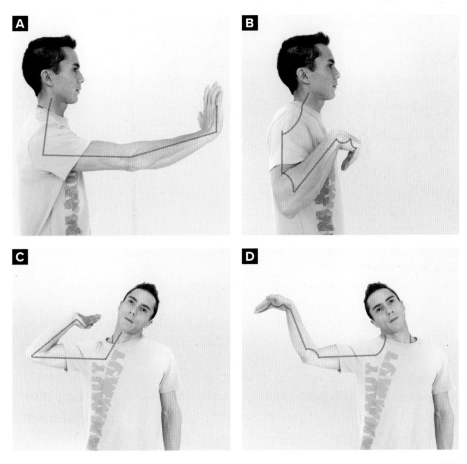

How to Know if a Nerve is Causing Your Pain

One test to identify if you have nerve pain is to put your arm in a nerve-tensioned position (see previous page for examples) and then move your neck. Only perform this test under supervision and clearance from a medical professional as it may cause increased symptoms. Once you are in the nerve-tensioned position, tilt your ear to the same side shoulder and opposite side shoulder. If your symptoms in the arm or hand change with head movement, then your pain is likely related to the nerve, and not the muscles, since there is no single muscle that attaches continuously from the neck down to the arm, wrist hand and fingers. The primary structure that can change tension with head movement is the nerve.

Use Nerve Motion to Treat Pain

You can use the dynamic properties of peripheral nerves to treat nerve related pain from a compressed nerve that is lacking mobility. Since nerves glide several millimeters between interfaces of muscle, you can glide nerves back and forth to increase their excursion and you can tension them to improve their capacity to withstand strain. Just don't stretch nerves statically like you would stretch a muscle—nerves don't respond well to sustained stretches. If you stretch a nerve with a sustained hold, the nerve can lose oxygen and blood flow. This can lead to further irritation of the nerve. This is the reason why you can sometimes feel "pins and needles" from a sustained stretch.

Nerve Glide Levels

Since nerves have extra play, they can be tensioned or slackened in different body positions. The next few pages will show you how to glide the median, ulnar and radial nerves through their respective muscular interfaces. There are two levels of exercise given to mobilize each nerve in this chapter. Level 1 is a gentle mobilization that utilizes alternating positions of slack and tension. Level 2 is a stronger mobilization that utilizes mostly tensioned positions.

How to Perform and How Often

All nerve glides should be performed for three sets of up to eight repetitions. Perform daily once you can glide the nerve without pain. The motion should be fluid and rhythmic. Never hold tension for more than two seconds at the end position. Start gentle with Level 1 exercises and progress to Level 2 exercises once you can perform Level 1 with ease and no pain. Discontinue nerve glides if you experience an increase in numbness and/or tingling. Nerves are sensitive and the mobilizations described in this chapter should be performed with care. To explore this topic in more detail, I highly recommend reading the book Neurodynamic Techniques written by the NOI Group.

Median Nerve Mobility Level 1

Instructions
A Extend your wrist and fingers backwards with your elbow bent.
B Press your arm straight while keeping your wrist and fingers extended.
C Flex your wrist and fingers downwards to the ground.
D Pull your arm back into a bend.

What It Does
A, B Tensions the median nerve at the wrist, elbow and fingers.
C, D Slackens the median nerve at the wrist, elbow and fingers improving the excursion of the median nerve.

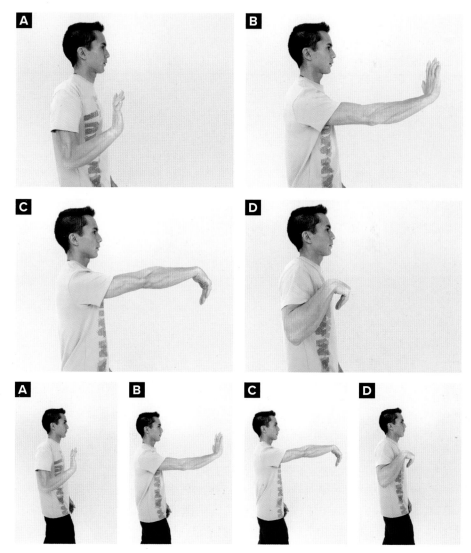

Median Nerve Mobility Level 2

Instructions

A Bend your shoulder and elbow back while touching the fingertips with your other hand.

B Press your arm down and extend your wrist back with the other hand.

C Keep your wrist pressed back and begin to raise your arm in the air.

D Press your wrist further back as you raise your arm higher in the air.

What It Does

A, B Tensions the median nerve at the wrist, elbow and fingers.

C, D Tensions the median nerve even more at the wrist, elbow and fingers improving the elongation and excursion of the median nerve.

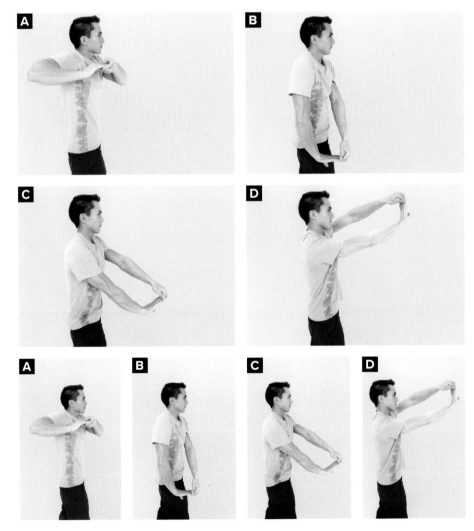

Ulnar Nerve Mobility Level 1

Instructions
A Extend your wrist and fingers backwards, bend your elbow and lean your head to the same side of the bent arm.

B Press your arm straight while you bend your head to the opposite side.

What It Does
A Tensions the ulnar nerve at the wrist, elbow and fingers but slackens the nerve at the neck.

B Slackens the ulnar nerve at the elbow but tensions the nerve at the neck improving the excursion of the ulnar nerve.

Ulnar Nerve Mobility Level 2

Instructions
A Flex your wrist and fingers forwards, bend your elbow to 90 degrees and lean your head to the same side of the bent arm.

B Extend your wrist and fingers backwards, bend your elbow even further and lean your head to the opposite side of the bent arm.

What It Does
A Slackens the ulnar nerve at the neck, elbow, wrist and fingers.

B Tensions the ulnar nerve at the neck, elbow, wrist and fingers improving the elongation and excursion of the ulnar nerve.

A

B

Radial Nerve Mobility Level 1

Instructions
A Interlock your hands and fingers together with your elbows slightly bent. The arm with the nerve injury should be on bottom.

B Bring your elbows upwards as high as possible while maintaining interlocked fingers.

What It Does
A Slackens the radial nerve at the elbow and tensions it at the wrist.

B Tensions the radial nerve at the wrist and further slackens it at the elbow improving the excursion of the radial nerve.

Tips
If the nerve is still irritated when performing this exercise, try shrugging your shoulders when you bring your wrists upwards. This may slacken the nerve as it exits through the neck and make this exercise easier to perform. If it is still a challenge, only bring your wrists up as far as comfortable.

A

B

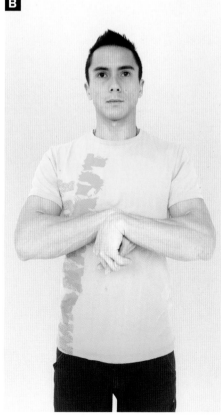

Radial Nerve Mobility Level 2

Instructions
A Straighten your wrist, elbow and fingers. Shrug your shoulder upwards.

B Flex your wrist and fingers and rotate your hand backwards a position as if you were to receive a cash tip. Lower your shoulder blade slightly and lean your head to the opposite side of the bent arm.

What It Does
A Slackens the radial nerve at the neck, elbow, wrist and fingers.

B Tensions the radial nerve at the neck, elbow, wrist and fingers improving the elongation and excursion of the radial nerve.

Tips
To make this mobilization more aggressive, try lowering your shoulder blade further downwards as you lean your head to the opposite side. This will increase the tension of the nerve as it exits the neck. To tension even more, tuck your thumb underneath your fingers.

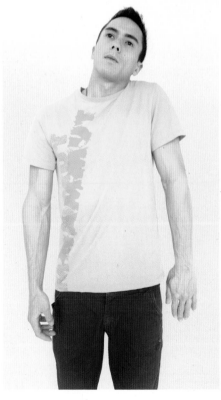 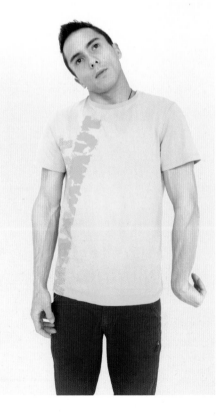

CHAPTER 8

THE DESCENT

Rock Rehab Pyramid appendix, research
references, profiles and services

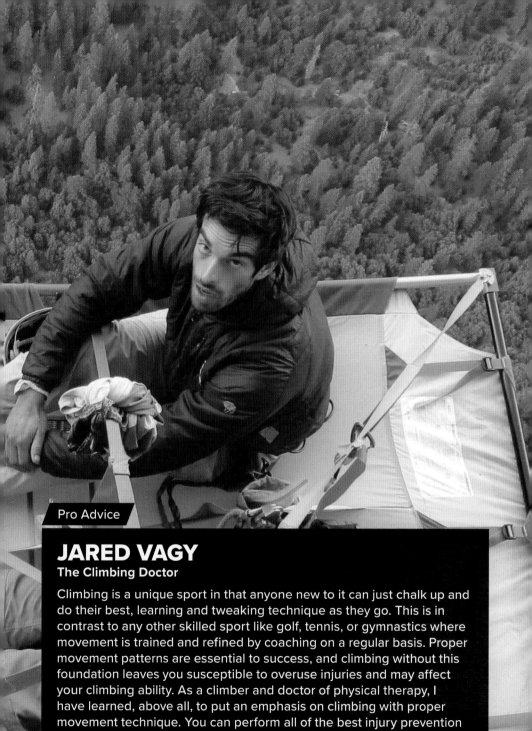

JARED VAGY
The Climbing Doctor

Climbing is a unique sport in that anyone new to it can just chalk up and do their best, learning and tweaking technique as they go. This is in contrast to any other skilled sport like golf, tennis, or gymnastics where movement is trained and refined by coaching on a regular basis. Proper movement patterns are essential to success, and climbing without this foundation leaves you susceptible to overuse injuries and may affect your climbing ability. As a climber and doctor of physical therapy, I have learned, above all, to put an emphasis on climbing with proper movement technique. You can perform all of the best injury prevention exercises, but if you are climbing with poor technique, it is only a matter of time before you get hurt.

Jeremy Eng (left) and Jared Vagy (right) on the Nose of El Capitan. Yosemite, CA. Photo Credit: Tara Misiewicz

ROCK REHAB PYRAMID APPENDIX

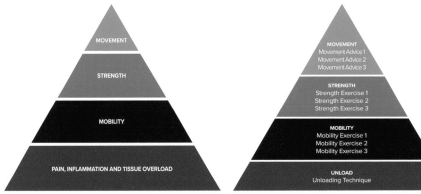

The Rock Rehab Pyramid: Page 54

Rock Rehab Breakdown: Page 55

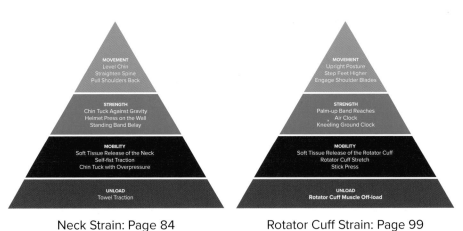

Neck Strain: Page 84

Rotator Cuff Strain: Page 99

Shoulder Impingement: Page 118

Biceps Tendinopathy: Page 129

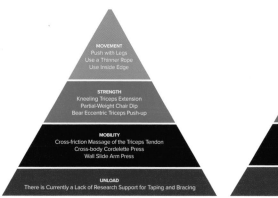

Triceps Tendinopathy: Page 140

Lateral Epicondylosis: Page 156

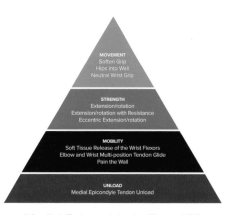

Medial Epicondylosis: Page 166

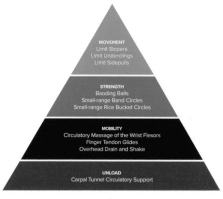

Carpal Tunnel Syndrome: Page 184

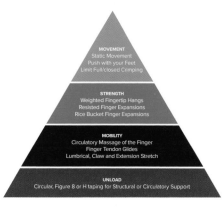

Pulley Sprain: Page 203

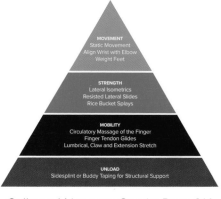

Collateral Ligament Sprain: Page 214

REFERENCES

CHAPTER 2: PREVENT INJURY

1. Aguilar AJ, DiStefano LJ, Brown CN, Herman DC, Guskiewicz KM, Padua D. A dynamic warm-up model increases quadriceps strength and hamstring flexibility. J Strength Cond Res. 2012 Apr;26(4):1130-41.

2. Doran, D. A., and M. Reay. "Injuries and associated training and performance characteristics in recreational rock climbers." Messenger N, W, Patterson W, Brook D (eds) The science of climbing and mountaineering. Human Kinetics, Champaign, IL (2000).

3. McMillian DJ, Moore JH, Hatler BS, Taylor DC. Dynamic vs. static-stretching warm up: the effect on power and agility performance. J Strength Cond Res. 2006 Aug;20(3):492-9.

4. Sim AY, Dawson BT, Guelfi KJ, Wallman KE, Young WB. Effects of static stretching in warm-up on repeated sprint performance. J Strength Cond Res. 2009 Oct;23(7):2155-62.

5. Gelen E. Acute effects of different warm-up methods on sprint, slalom dribbling, and penalty kick performance in soccer players. J Strength Cond Res. 2010 Apr;24(4): 950-6.

6. Sayers AL et al. The effect of static stretching on phases of sprint performance in elite soccer players. J Strength Cond Res. 2008 Sep;22(5):1416-21.

7. Fletcher Iet al. The acute effects of combined static and dynamic stretch protocols on fifty-meter sprint performance in track-and-field athletes. J Strength Cond Res. 2007 Aug;21(3):784-7.

8. Neil Gresham. Improve your climbing with Neil Gresham maser class part 1. Film. 2005.

9. Anderson, Michael L., and Mark L. Anderson. The Rock Climber's Training Manual: A Guide to Continuous Improvement. Fixed Pin, Colorado, 2014. Print.

CHAPTER 3: THE ROCK REHAB PYRAMID

1. Moayedi, Massieh, and Karen D. Davis. "Theories of pain: from specificity to gate control." Journal of neurophysiology 109.1 (2013): 5-12.

2. C. Taber, K. Contryman, J. Fahrenbruch, K. LaCount, M. W. Cornwall. Measurement of Reactive Vasodilation During Cold Gel Pack Application to Nontraumatized Ankles. Phys Ther. April. 1992 72:294-299.

3. Webb JM, Williams D, Ivory JP, Day S, Williamson DM. The use of cold compression dressings after total knee replacement: a randomized controlled trial. Orthopedics 21 1998. (1): 59–61.

4. Ohkoshi Y, Ohkoshi M, Nagasaki S, Ono A, Hashimoto T, Yamane S. The effect of cryotherapy on intraarticular temperature and postoperative care after anterior cruciate ligament reconstruction. Am J Sports Med 27. 1999. 357–62.

5. Martin et al. Cryotherapy: an effective modality for decreasing intraarticular temperature after knee arthroscopy. Am J Sports Med. 2001. 288–91.

6. Chen et al. The effect of nonsteroidal anti-inflammatory drugs on tissue healing. Knee Surg Sports Traumatol Arthrosc. 2013 Mar;21. 540-9.

7. Eiff, Smith AT, Smith GE. Early mobilization versus immobilization in the treatment of lateral ankle sprains. J Sports Med. 1994 Jan-Feb;22(1):83-8.

8. Perrin, David. Athletic Taping and Bracing Book-3rd Edition. Human Kinetics, 2012.

CHAPTER 4: SHOULDER AND NECK

Neck Strain

1. Aker PD, Gross AR, Goldsmith CH, Peloso P. Conservative management of mechanical neck pain: systematic overview and meta-analysis. BMJ. 1996;313:1291–1296.

2. Uhlig Y, Weber BR, Grob D, Muntener M. Fiber composition and fiber transformations in neck muscles of patients with dysfunction of the cervical spine. J Orthop Res. 1995;13:240–249.

3. Harris KD, Heer DM, Roy TC, et al. Measurement characteristics of a test of deep neck flexor muscle endurance in individuals with and without neck pain. Phys Ther. 2005;85:1349–1355.

4. Silverman JL, Rodriquez AA, Agre JC. Quantitative cervical flexor strength in healthy subjects and in subjects with mechanical neck pain. Arch Phys Med Rehabil. 1991;72:679–681.

5. Norlander S, Nordgren B. Clinical symptoms related to musculoskeletal neck-shoulder pain and mobility in the cervico-thoracic spine. Scand J Rehabil Med. 1998;30:243–251.

6. Panjabi MM. The stabilizing system of the spine. Part I. Function, dysfunction, adaptation, and enhancement. J Spinal Disord. 1992;5:383–389.

Rotator Cuff Strain

1. Malliou PC, Giannakopoulos K, Beneka AG, Gioftsidou A, Godolias G. Effective ways of restoring muscular imbalances of the RTC muscle group: a comparative study of various training methods. Br J Sports Med. 2004;38:766–772.

2. Reinold MM et al. EMG analysis of the rotator cuff and deltoid musculature during common shoulder external rotation exercises. J Orthop Sports Phys Ther. 2004;34:385–394.

3. Van der Heijden GJ et al. Physiotherapy for patients with soft tissue shoulder disorders: a systematic review of randomized clinical trials. BMJ. 1997;315:25–30.

4. Malanga GA, Jenp YN, Growney ES, et al. EMG analysis of shoulder positioning in testing and strengthening the supraspinatus. Med Sci Sports Exerc. 1996;28:661–664.

5. Kramer WJ, Ratamess NA. Fundamentals of resistance training: progression and exercise prescription. Med Sci Sports Exerc. 2004;36:674–688.

6. Ellenbecker TS, Davies GJ. Closed Kinetic Chain Exercise: A Comprehensive Guide to Multiple Joint Exercise. Champaign, Ill: Human Kinetics;2001.

Shoulder Impingement

1. Michener LA, McClure PW, Karduna AR. Anatomical and biomechanical mechanisms of subacromial impingement syndrome. Clin Biomech. 2003;18:369–379.

2. Blasier et al. Anterior shoulder stability: contributions of rotator cuff forces and the capsular ligaments in a cadaver model. J Shoulder Elbow Surg. 1992;1:140–150.

3. Itoi E, Berglund LJ, Grabowski JJ, Naggar L, Morrey BF, An KN. Superior-inferior stability of the shoulder: role of the coracohumeral ligament and the rotator interval capsule. Mayo Clin Proc. 1998;73: 508–515.

4. Flatow EL, Soslowsky LJ, Ticker JB, et al. Excursion of the rotator cuff under the acromion. Patterns of subacromial contact. Am J Sports Med. 1994;22: 779–788.

CHAPTER 5: ELBOW

Biceps Tendinopathy

1. Ahrens, P. M., and P. Boileau. The long head of biceps and associated tendinopathy. Journal of Bone & Joint Surgery, British Volume 89.8 (2007): 1001-1009.

2. Eakin, Colin L., et al. Biceps tendon disorders in athletes. Journal of the American Academy of Orthopaedic Surgeons 7.5 (1999): 300-310.

3. Nho, Shane J., et al. Long head of the biceps tendinopathy: diagnosis and management.Journal of the American Academy of Orthopaedic Surgeons 18.11 (2010): 645-656.

4. Schamblin, Mark L., and Marc R. Safran. Injury of the distal biceps at the musculotendinous junction. Journal of Shoulder and Elbow Surgery 16.2 (2007): 208-212.

5. Ervilha, Ulysses F., et al. The effect of muscle pain on elbow flexion and coactivation tasks. Experimental brain research 156.2 (2004): 174-182.

Triceps Tendinopathy

1. Ginszt, Michał, et al. Climbing injuries among children and youth. (2011).

2. Taylor, Samuel A., and Jo A. Hannafin. Evaluation and management of elbow tendinopathy. Sports Health: A Multidisciplinary Approach 4.5 (2012): 384-393.

3. Gabel, Gerard "Acute and chronic tendinopathies at the elbow." Current opinion in rheumatology (1999): 138-143.

Lateral Epicondylosis

1. Haahr JP, Andersen JH. Physical and psychosocial risk factors for lateral epicondylitis: a population based case-referent study. Occup Environ Med. 2003;60:322–329.

2. Smidt N, Asssendelft W, Arola H, et al. Effectiveness of physiotherapy for lateral epicondylitis: a systematic review. Ann Med. 2003;35:51–62.

3. An KN, Hui FC, Morrey BF, Linscheid RL, Chao EY. Muscles across the elbow joint: a biomechanical analysis. J Biomech. 1981;14:659–669.

4. Pienimäki T, Tarvainen T, Siira P, Vanharanta JH. Progressive strengthening and stretching exercises for chronic lateral epicondylitis. Physiotherapy. 1996;82:522–530.

5. O'Driscoll SW, Horii E, Ness R, Cahalan TD, Richards RR, An KN. The relationship between wrist position, grasp size, and grip strength. J Hand Surg Am. 1992 Jan;17(1):169-77.

6. Vicenzino B, et al. Initial effects of elbow taping on pain-free grip strength and pressure pain threshold. J Orthop Sports Phys Ther. 2003;33(7):400-7.

Medial Epicondylosis

1. Ciccotti MG. Diagnosis and treatment of medial epicondylitis of the elbow. Clin Sports Med. 2004;23:693–705. 61.

2. Galloway M, DeMaio M, Mangine R. Rehabilitative techniques in the treatment of medial and lateral epicondylitis. Orthopedics. 1992;15:1089–1096.

CHAPTER 6: WRIST AND FINGERS

Carpal Tunnel Syndrome

1. Holtzhausen, Lucy-May, and Timothy D. Noakes. Elbow, forearm, wrist, and hand injuries among sport rock climbers. Clinical Journal of Sport Medicine 6.3 (1996): 196-203.

2. Rozmaryn, Leo M., et al. Nerve and tendon gliding exercises and the conservative management of carpal tunnel syndrome. Journal of Hand Therapy 11.3 (1998): 171-179.

Pulley Sprain

1. Silfverskiold KL, May EJ. Flexor tendon repair in zone 2 with a new suture technique and an early mobilization program combining passive and active motion. J Hand Surg 1994;19A:53–60.

2. Groth GN. Pyramid of progressive force exercises to the injured flexor tendon. J Hand Ther 2004;17(1): 31–42.

3. Hochholzer, Thomas, and Volker Schöffl. One move too many. Lochner Verlag, Ebenhausen, Germany (2006).

4. Horst, Eric. Training for climbing. Helena, Montana: Falcon Guides. December 1, 2002.

5. Bollen, S. R. Soft tissue injury in extreme rock climbers. British Journal of Sports Medicine 22.4 (1988): 145-147.

6. Quaine, Franck, et al. The thumb during the crimp grip. International journal of sports medicine 32.1 (2011): 49.

7. Schöffl I, Einwag F, Strecker W, Hennig F, Schöffl V (2007) Impact of taping after finger flexor tendon pulley ruptures in rock climbers. J Appl Biomech 23, 52-62.

8. Anderson, Michael et al. An Innovative Hangboard Design to Improve Finger Strength in Rock Climbers. Procedia Engineering 147 (2016): 269-274.

Collateral Ligament Sprain

1. Bollen, S. R., and C. K. Gunson. Hand injuries in competition climbers. British journal of sports Medicine 24.1 (1990): 16-18.

2. Rohrbough, Joel et al. Overuse injuries in the elite rock climber. Medicine and science in sports and exercise 32.8 (2000): 1369-1372.

CHAPTER 7: NERVE MOBILITY

1. Byl, Carolyn, et al. Strain in the median and ulnar nerves during upper-extremity positioning. The Journal of hand surgery 27.6 (2002): 1032-1040.

2. Coppieters et al. Different nerve-gliding exercises induce different magnitudes of median nerve longitudinal excursion: an in vivo study using dynamic ultrasound imaging. journal of orthopaedic & sports physical therapy 39.3 (2009): 164-171.

3. Butler, David Sheridan, ed. The neurodynamic techniques: a definitive guide from the Noigroup team. Noigroup publications, 2005.

4. USC Division of Biokinesiology and Physical Therapy. Neurodynamics. PT 621 lab handbook. Los Angeles, California. 2017.

ABOUT THE FEATURED CLIMBERS

Sasha DiGiulian

Sasha is the first North American woman to climb the grade 5.14d, which is still recognized as the hardest sport climb rating ever achieved by a female. Sasha was the third woman in the world to accomplish this grade. She has done two. She has onsighted multiple 5.14a's, ascended groundbreaking multipitch routes of up to 1,000 feet of 5.14b climbing, and has accomplished multiple first ascents and 28 first female ascents around the world. Sasha is a former indoor rock climbing world champion for the category female overall. She has placed silver in the bouldering world championships and has placed bronze in the duel.

Jonathan Siegrist

Jonathan is a passionate professional climber and global traveler. He spends his years primarily on the road and overseas, constantly on a mission to develop new areas and pursue the challenge and beauty in hard rock climbing. Since he began his journey with climbing at age 18 he has step by step experimented and refined his methods of training for a variety of goals. Now, at 30, his career highlights include 196 5.14 ascents, 5.14 traditional routes, many 5.14 flashes including one at 5.14b, dozens of first ascents, several big walls up to 5.13+ and several ascents of 5.15a including Biographie, La Rambla, Power Inverter and Papichulo.

ABOUT THE FEATURED CLIMBERS

Sean McColl

Sean McColl is an avid 28-year-old professional climber. During his youth career, he claimed 5 Youth World Championship titles; this achievement is unsurpassed in youth climbing history to this day. Since Sean started competing on the World Cup circuit, he has won 4 World Cups and has been on the podium at 29 events. Sean is a 3-time Adult World Champion and has been 2nd and 3rd in the Lead and Boulder Overall rankings. As an outdoor climber, Sean has onsighted 5.14a and climbed multiple 5.14d's. On the bouldering side, Sean is one of a dozen climbers in the world to flash the grade of V13 and redpoint V15.

Josh Levin

Josh Levin is recognized as USA Climbing's most successful youth competitor. He spent his early climbing career accumulating 19 national championship titles, 5 continental championships, multiple USA speed climbing records, and the bronze medal at the 2008 youth world championships. He has won in the pro circuit in bouldering, sport climbing, and speed climbing competitions, establishing himself as one of the most well-rounded competitors in the sport. With over 16 years of climbing experience, Josh has ticked off V12 and 5.14c outdoors, and is the athlete representative on the USA climbing board of directors.

ABOUT THE PHOTOGRAPHERS

The photographs in this book would not have been possible without the support of these three photographers:

Ari Kirsch: Arikirschphoto.com
Stephen Gross: Ssgphoto.com
Matthew Johnson: Matthewjohnson.tumblr.com

Much gratitude also goes out to the professional photographers that have kindly contributed their athlete photos to this humble offering.

Their stellar work is worth checking out and you can help support them by purchasing their photographs.

Janelle Anderson
Chris Alstrin: Alstrinfilms.com
Andrew Burr: Andrewburr.com
Tommy Chandler: Tommychandler.com
Adam Demmert: Adamds.smugmug.com
Eddie Fowke: Thecircuitclimbing.com
Daniel Holz: Danholzphotography.com
Alexandra Kahn: Asinspiredmedia.com
Anthony Lapomardo
Luke Olsen: Lukeolsonphotography@gmail.com
Javier Pérez López-Triviño: Javipec.com
Cameron Maier: Bearcammedia.com
Stella Marchisio
Jesse Peters
Jon D. Petersen: Jonpetersen@sbcglobal.net
Christine Bailey Speed: Christinebaileyspeed.com
Jim Thornburg: Jimthornburg.com
Jensen Walker: Jensenwalker.com

A SPECIAL THANKS TO THE PROFILED CLIMBERS

Mike Anderson, Christian Core, Steph Davis, Hans Florine, Hazel Findlay, Dan Mirsky, Adam Ondra, Ethan Pringle, Paul Robinson, Ben Rueck, Mayan Smith-Gobat, Sonnie Trotter and Vasya Vorotnikov.

ABOUT THE AUTHOR

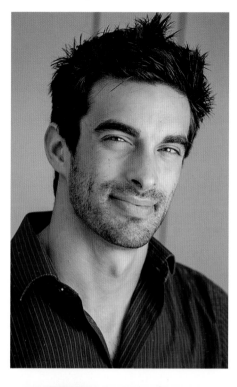

Professional Life

Jared Vagy is a doctor of physical therapy who specializes in treating climbing injuries. In addition to his doctoral degree, he has completed a one-year residency in orthopedics and a one-year fellowship in movement science, totaling 9 years of concentrated study. He has published numerous articles on injury prevention and lectures on the topic internationally. Dr. Vagy is on the faculty at the University of Southern California, the number-one-ranked doctor of physical therapy program in the United States. He is a board certified orthopedic clinical specialist and a certified strength and conditioning specialist.

Climbing Life

Jared Vagy has over 14 years of climbing experience and has climbed all over the world. He is an accomplished rock climber, ice climber and alpinist, and continues to explore the wonders of adventure that these pursuits afford.

IN-PERSON EVALUATION

This opportunity is available if you live in or can travel to Los Angeles. During the evaluation, your mobility, muscle strength, movement and climbing technique are assessed and scored to give you a personal blueprint of your body, identifying all asymmetries and imbalances. This information serves as an important guide to help you rehabilitate or prevent injury so that you can climb harder without getting hurt.

Contact: Jared@theclimbingdoctor.com to schedule

REMOTE CONSULTATION

If you are unable to travel to Los Angeles but would like to consult with The Climbing Doctor, remote consultation is an option. To do so, you will need to photograph your posture, video yourself climbing and submit the footage for analysis. This information will be used during a Skype session to answer your questions and develop a plan to climb stronger and injury-free.

Jared Vagy will operate under his strength and conditioning certification to provide a wellness consultation

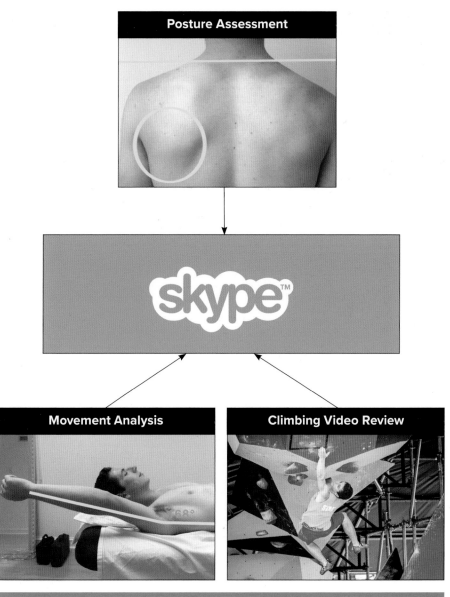

Contact: Jared@theclimbingdoctor.com to schedule

CLIMB INJURY-FREE CLINICS AND LECTURES

In-Person Clinics
Injury-prevention clinics teach the necessary skills needed to prevent injury. They are held at climbing festivals, organizations, gyms or as private events. Clinic sizes range from small groups of 8-12 climbers to large groups of up to 50 climbers.

In-Person Lectures
Climb injury-free lectures are given at corporate events, symposiums and conferences. Lecture audiences can range from 50-400 climbers.

Webinar Clinics
On-line-based clinics provide an easy way to access live injury prevention clinics from your computer, tablet or phone.

Clinics and lectures utilize a variety of rehabilitation tools to teach preventative exercises. All content can be customized to the specific setting where the clinic is being held.

Contact: Jared@theclimbingdoctor.com to schedule

PRO CLIMBER TESTIMONIALS

Sasha DiGiulian
World Champion Climber

The evaluation detailed the fine specifics of my climbing technique and related it to my strengths and weaknesses. It was really useful. I can totally feel what Dr. Vagy says about how my muscles have imbalances. So seeing that and thinking how I can apply the information to my own climbing was key. The evaluation gives awareness to what you are doing right and wrong and will help you seek gains in your own performance.

Jonathan Siegrist
5.15 Sport Climber and Adventurer

The evaluation was a thorough, hands-on investigation into my body's imbalances, strengths and weaknesses. It gave me answers and suggestions for moving forward as an athlete. Dr. Vagy is a knowledgeable consultant with a clearly enormous understanding of movement and the athletic body. It has really made a difference in my climbing. I attribute my success this year climbing to a lot of the knowledge he taught me.

Josh Levin
19-Time Youth National Champion

There are no other evaluations in the United States that give as full of a picture of climbing than with Dr. Vagy. You learn exactly what is needed to stay healthy in the long-term. A climber of any level can benefit from this evaluation no matter if you're just starting out or are a seasoned pro who's been climbing for most of their life. I highly recommend Dr. Vagy if you are seeking to boost your climbing performance.

Matt Segal
5.14 Traditional Climb First Ascensionist

I love climbing and at the end of the day Dr. Vagy helps me stay injury-free and climb stronger. The climber evaluation is one of the most helpful learning experiences. Dr. Vagy helped me come to my own conclusions about my body and movement in relation to climbing. It wasn't just a simple diagnostic but a discussion and education on how to train and prevent injuries to keep me doing what I love.

PRO CLIMBER TESTIMONIALS

Mayan Smith-Gobat
Women's Speed Record on The Nose

The remote consultation would be a huge benefit to climbers to learn to use your body more efficiently. Gaining strength in a more balanced way to promote long-term health and help prevent injury. The videos made the remote consultation very interactive. I thought it was excellent, above my expectations for sure!

Dan Mirsky
5.14c Sport Climb First Ascensionist

Dr. Vagy does an excellent job of analyzing and presenting a cohesive picture of how your body works and doesn't work, your movement patterns and muscle imbalances. He helps you to achieve an understanding about the connectivity of your body so you can fix problems, heal injuries, improve strength and flexibility all in a truly effective long-term way.

Hazel Findlay
First British Woman to Climb an E9 Trad Route

Working with Dr. Vagy has been really beneficial for my shoulder! The remote consultation is extremely helpful in understanding the nature of your injury and learning exactly how to fix it. It is very scientific. It's perfect for people who travel because it doesn't require continuous visits to the Physio and gives you a targeted plan of exercises which can be done anywhere.

Mike Anderson
Developer of the Rock Prodigy Training Method

To have an in-person evaluation from Dr. Vagy was very helpful and I feel fortunate to have that opportunity. He is a climber and the expert in Physical Therapy for climbing injuries. He knows how to target detailed assessments specifically to climbing. At my age for as long as I have been climbing, I'm looking for any way to improve. Dr. Vagy was able to identify a huge potential area for me and I'm now super psyched to work on that.

CLIMBER TESTIMONIALS: REMOTE CONSULTATION

Joel Rocha
Redlands, California

The peace-of-mind that comes from having a professional opinion on my injury cannot be overstated. I could've self-diagnosed via the Internet, or seen some practitioner unfamiliar with climbing, and never actually gotten any closer to figuring out what I need to do to "fix" myself. But because Dr. Vagy understands the positions and forces that we climbers subject ourselves to, I can fully trust his injury diagnosis and rehab plan.

Olivier Plamondon
Quebec, Canada

There are no viable doctors or physios available that I know of in North America that could help me with my climbing injury; except Dr. Vagy. Climbing puts stresses that are so specific that not doing this type of consultation can result in months and even years of time lost. Dr. Vagy is professional, very organized and thorough. It is obvious that he has done a lot of research and stays on top of the literature. He rocks, basically.

Devin Doyle
Busan, South Korea

Dr. Vagy is a tremendous resource for the climbing community. The level of knowledge that he provides is extremely pragmatic. With his advice, you will not only be able to understand your injury better and rehab it, but you'll get a functional approach which will teach you improved movement patterns when on and off the wall. This will keep you healthy not only right after your injury, but further into your climbing career.

Ian Mulvany
London, England

I just got back from a short 4-day trip to Spain and I redpointed 5.11c (6c+). To put that in context, the last time I climbed harder was back in 2004. A huge amount of that is down to the consultation that we did, and the confidence it gave me to return to training. I learned how to fix my elbow, and how to pay more attention to the way that I put power through my shoulders!

CLIMBER TESTIMONIALS: IN-PERSON EVALUATION

Grae Halsne
Sport Climber Looking to Push His Limits

The traditional doctor or even specialist will never give enough information to satisfy the climber. The climber needs more beta! Dr. Vagy is able to give the most crucial beta that no one else has available since the guide book is still at the printer. I really appreciate the hands-on approach that understands the climbers body, mentality and pursuit of the climb.

Gina Edwards
Traditional Climber Living on the Road

Being evaluated would be highly beneficial to any climber who is struggling with injury, concerned with preventing future injury, and holds value in their ability to climb safe and strong for many years. One of the biggest benefits is knowing that a doctor truly understands the sport and therefore I feel very confident with his diagnosis and follow-up plan.

Justin Moynihan
Boulderer and AMGA Certified Rock Instructor

Today my Achilles heel (as a climber) was revealed to me in photographs of my asymmetrical body, reinforced by unbalanced strength and flexibility tests, and further shown in my form as I move rock climbing. This is the answer to why I could not train as hard as I wanted to in the past. I now have put Dr. Vagy's recovery and training suggestions into practice and have sent harder than ever before without the limitation of injury.

Thea Wulff
From the Parent of a Youth Competitive Climber

The evaluation was more comprehensive than I could have imagined for my daughter. The evaluation was thorough, specific, clear and concise. It was extremely detailed and included personal photos with computer-drawn lines over the body to show spine curvature, scrunched shoulders, etc. In addition to being knowledgeable and helpful, Dr. Vagy was super nice... You can't ask for anything more!